SINGING EVERY DAY

ENLARGED EDITION

By   **LILLA BELLE PITTS**
Professor Emeritus of Music Education
Teachers College, Columbia University, New York

MABELLE GLENN
Formerly Director of Music
Public Schools, Kansas City, Missouri

LORRAIN E. WATTERS
Director of Music
Public Schools, Des Moines, Iowa

and   **LOUIS G. WERSEN**
Director of Music Education
Public Schools, Philadelphia, Pennsylvania

ILLUSTRATIONS BY Ruth Wood, Alison Cummings, Eloise Wilkin, and Beryl Bailey-Jones

GINN AND COMPANY

BOSTON · NEW YORK · CHICAGO · ATLANTA · DALLAS · PALO ALTO · TORONTO · LONDON

Acknowledgments

Acknowledgment is due to publishers, composers, and authors for permission to reprint songs and poems in this book, as follows:

MARJORIE BARROWS, "Three Little Witches"; BRADBURY, AGNEW & COMPANY, LIMITED, lines from "Noise," by J. POPE; PAUL BURLIN, "Cradle Song" and "Song of the Spirit-Dance," from *The Indians' Book*, by NATALIE CURTIS; JESSIE CARTER AND CHRISTINE L. CHISHOLM, "Little Carl Must Go to Rest," translated by H. JACOBSON; CHURCHILL-GRINDELL COMPANY, "Moon's Lullaby," from *Song Book No. III*, copyright 1910, 1938 by CHURCHILL-GRINDELL COMPANY; J. CURWEN & SONS, LTD., "For Health and Strength," from *Graded Rounds and Catches*, Curwen Edition 6079, by permission; *The Christian Science Monitor* and the author, "Jack Frost," by HELEN BAYLEY DAVIS; EXPRESSION COMPANY, "The North Wind," from *Speech Improvement through Choral Speaking*; HARCOURT, BRACE AND COMPANY, "Ships," from *Magpie Lane*, by NANCY BYRD TURNER, copyright 1927 by HARCOURT, BRACE AND COMPANY, INC.; GINN AND COMPANY, "Crossing the Brook" and "San Sereni," from *The Latin-American Song Book*, copyright 1942; GINN AND COMPANY and the editors of THE WORLD OF MUSIC, "Four in a Boat," from *Tuning Up*, copyright 1936, 1943; "Down the Stream" and "Oopsy Daisy Oh!" from *Rhythms and Rimes*, copyright 1936, 1943; "The Bell Ringer," "Hungarian Dance," "Marching Song" (melody), "Quiet Night," and "Sung at Harvest Time," from *Songs of Many Lands*, copyright 1936, 1943; "O Jesu Sweet," "The Polka," and "Rivers of China" from *On Wings of Song*, copyright 1945; HOUGHTON MIFFLIN COMPANY, "Her Hands" (excerpt) from *Shoes That Danced*, by ANNA HEMPSTEAD BRANCH, by permission of HOUGHTON MIFFLIN COMPANY; ALFRED A. KNOPF, "The Cowboy's Lament" ("My Home's in Montana"), reprinted from *Singing Cowboy*, by MARGARET LARKIN, copyright 1931, by permission of ALFRED A. KNOPF, INC.; J. B. LIPPINCOTT COMPANY, "Thanksgiving Day," from *For Days and Days*, by ANNETTE WYNNE, copyright 1919 by J. B. LIPPINCOTT COMPANY; THE MACMILLAN COMPANY, "Ferry Me across the Water," from *Poetical Works*, by CHRISTINA ROSSETTI, two lines of "Joy," from *Rivers to the Sea*, by SARA TEASDALE, copyright 1915 by THE MACMILLAN COMPANY and used with their permission, and "High, Betty Martin" and "The Old Sow Song" ("The Sow with the Measles"), from *Folk Songs of Old New England*, by ELOISE HUBBARD LINSCOTT, copyright 1939 by THE MACMILLAN COMPANY and used with their permission; DR. MARÍA CADILLA DE MARTÍNEZ, "The Brown Bird," from *Cantos y Juegos Infantiles*, by DR. MARTÍNEZ; THE OXFORD UNIVERSITY PRESS, "Mists of Daybreak" and "The Sunrise Tints the Dew," from *A Year of Japanese Epigrams*, by WILLIAM N. PORTER; PENNSYLVANIA MILITARY COLLEGE, "Night Song"; PRESBYTERIAN COLLEAGUES, INC., "Rise Up, O Men of God," by WILLIAM PIERSON MERRILL, from *The Presbyterian Tribune*; THEODORE PRESSER COMPANY, "Lullaby," from *American Negro Songs and Spirituals*, by JOHN W. WORK, as published and copyrighted (1940) by THEODORE PRESSER COMPANY, used by permission; FLEMING H. REVELL COMPANY, "Hear Our Prayer, O Lord," by GEORGE WHELPTON, from *New Hymnal for American Youth*; G. SCHIRMER, INC., "The Angel Band," from *Thirty-Six South Carolina Spirituals*. Used by permission of the copyright owner, G. SCHIRMER, INC.; VIOLET ALLEYN STOREY, "Rainy Day Song," from *Child Life*; JANET TOBITT, "Hush-a-bye, Birdie," from *Yours for a Song*; ALMA A. TURECHEK, "Whither, Little Path," copyright 1943 by ALMA A. TURECHEK; LOUIS UNTERMEYER, "Spring Ring Jingle" ("Fol-de-rol and Riddle-ma-ree"), by MICHAEL LEWIS, from *Rainbow in the Sky*, published by HARCOURT, BRACE AND COMPANY; THE VIKING PRESS, two stanzas of "Father's Story," from *Under the Tree*, by ELIZABETH MADOX ROBERTS, copyright 1922 by B. W. HUEBSCH, INC., reprinted by permission of THE VIKING PRESS, INC., New York; "Susan Blue," by KATE GREENAWAY, by permission of FREDERICK WARNE & Co., INC. of New York, publishers of the Kate Greenaway Books in America, and FREDERICK WARNE & Co., LTD. of London, publishers of the Kate Greenaway Books in Canada; to RUTH CRAWFORD SEEGER for her assistance in collecting folk and traditional songs. "I Have a Little Valentine," by MARY C. PARSONS, was originally published in *The Youth's Companion*.

In the case of some poems for which acknowledgment is not given, we have earnestly endeavored to find the original source and to procure permission for their use, but without success.

Contents

SONGS WE KNOW · (Page 7)

[Titles in italics indicate instrumental selections.]

ABOUT FOLKS · (Page 15)

Happy Holidays

4

Song-book, Song-book,
What have you to say?
"Pick a song, short or long,
There's one for every day:
Monday, Tuesday, Wednesday, Thursday,
Friday, Saturday, Sunday, Monday.
Pick a song, short or long,
You shall sing today!"

Lilla Belle Pitts

SONGS WE KNOW

Johnny Schmoker

Traditional

John - ny Schmo - ker, John - ny Schmo - ker,

Can you sing, • can you play? •

1. I can play up - on my vi - o - lin.
2. I can play up - on my clar - i - net.
3. I can play up - on my sil - ver flute.

Fid - dle did - dle dee, so sings my vi - o - lin.
Doo - dle doo - dle doo, so sings my clar - i - net.
Too - tle too - tle toot, so sings my sil - ver flute.

4. Slide trombone - Taa-ta-ta-ta-taa, so sings my slide trombone.
5. New cornet   - Ta-ta-ta-ta-ta, so sings my new cornet.
6. Big bass drum - Boom-a-boom-a-boom, so sings my big bass drum.

After each stanza repeat the sounds of the instruments you sang in the earlier stanzas. Pretend to play each instrument as you sing. What instruments would you like to add to this song?

7

Polly-Wolly-Doodle

College Song

CHORDS:

1. Oh, I went down South to see my Sal,
2. Oh, my Sal-ly is a maid-en fair,

Sing Pol-ly-wol-ly-doo-dle all the day;
Sing Pol-ly-wol-ly-doo-dle all the day;

My Sal-ly is a spunk-y gal,
With curl-y eyes and laugh-ing hair,

Sing Pol-ly-wol-ly-doo-dle all the day.
Sing Pol-ly-wol-ly-doo-dle all the day.

CHORUS

Fare thee well, fare thee well, Fare thee well, my fair-y fay,

For I'm going to Loui-si-an-a, for to see my Su-sy-an-na,

8

Sing Pol - ly - wol - ly - doo - dle all the day.

3. Behind the barn, down on my knees,
   Sing Polly-wolly-doodle all the day;
   I thought I heard a chicken sneeze,
   Sing Polly-wolly-doodle all the day.

4. He sneezed so hard with whooping cough,
   Sing Polly-wolly-doodle all the day;
   He sneezed his head and tail right off,
   Sing Polly-wolly-doodle all the day.

Little Red Caboose

Camp Song

Lit - tle red ca - boose, lit - tle red ca - boose,

Lit - tle red ca - boose be - hind the train, · the train. ·

Smoke - stack on his back, go - ing down the track.

Lit - tle red ca-boose be-hind the train. · · · train. (Too-too-too!)

9

Home on the Range

Cowboy Song

Oh, give me a home where the buf - fa - lo roam,

Where the deer and the an - te - lope play,

Where sel - dom is heard a dis - cour - ag - ing word,

And the skies are not cloud - y all day.

Home, home on the range, · Where the deer and the an - te - lope play, ·

10

Where sel - dom is heard a dis - cour - ag - ing word,

And the skies are not cloud - y all day.

Susie, Little Susie

Translated from the German

German Folk Song
from "Hansel and Gretel"

1. Su - sie, lit - tle Su - sie, now what is the news?
2. Su - sie, lit - tle Su - sie, we are in a fix,

The geese are go - ing bare - foot be - cause they've no shoes.
No pen - nies for some sug - ar and no bread to mix.

The cob - bler has leath - er, but no last to use,
If I sell my bed, sleep on straw for the night,

So he can - not make them a pair of new shoes.
Feath - ers will not prick - le and fleas will not bite.

11

High, Betty Martin

Square Dance Song

High, Bet-ty Mar-tin, tip toe, tip toe,

High, · Bet-ty Mar-tin, tip toe fine.

Nev-er found a boy to suit her fan-cy,

Nev-er found a boy to suit her mind.

Tra la la la la la la la, Tra la la la la la la la,

Tra la la la, Bet-ty Mar-tin, please be mine.

Haul Away, Joe

Sea Chantey

SOLO

1. A - way, haul a - way, · Come haul a - way to - geth - er,
2. A - way, haul a - way, · I'll sing to you of Nan - cy,

CHORUS

A - way, haul a - way, · Haul a - way, Joe.

SOLO

A - way, haul a - way, · We'll haul for fin - er weath - er,
A - way, haul a - way, · She's just my style and fan - cy,

CHORUS

A - way, haul a - way, · We'll haul a - way, Joe.

13

Old MacDonald Had a Farm

Traditional

1. Old Mac-Don-ald had a farm, E - I - E - I - O!
2. Old Mac-Don-ald had a farm, E - I - E - I - O!
3. Old Mac-Don-ald had a farm, E - I - E - I - O!

And on this farm he had some chicks, E - I - E - I - O!
And on this farm he had some ducks, E - I - E - I - O!
And on this farm he had some tur-keys, E - I - E - I - O!

With a chick, chick here, and a chick, chick there,
With a quack, quack here, and a quack, quack there,
With a gob-ble, gob-ble, here, and a gob-ble, gob-ble there,

Here a chick, there a chick, ev-'ry-where a chick, chick.
Here a quack, there a quack, ev-'ry-where a quack, quack.
Here a gob-ble, there a gob-ble, ev-'ry-where a gob-ble, gob-ble.

Old Mac-Don-ald had a farm, E - I - E - I - O!
Old Mac-Don-ald had a farm, E - I - E - I - O!
Old Mac-Don-ald had a farm, E - I - E - I - O!

Additional stanzas may be sung about all the other farm animals you
know. With each new stanza it is fun to repeat the farmyard sounds in the
earlier stanzas, just before you sing the last line of the song.

ABOUT FOLKS

I like to see the people,
Lots and lots of people,
Crowding in the street;
Boys and girls a-racing,
Pushing, pulling, chasing
With prancy, dancy feet.

I like to hear the people,
Lots and lots of people,
Walking in and out;
Happy folks "Helloing,"
Sounds of footsteps going
Here and there and all about.

I like to be with people,
Lots and lots of people,
Smiling as they meet;
Fat and thin, short and tall,
Making funny shadows fall
All along the street.

L. B. P.

Playtime Songs

And young and old come forth to play
On a sunshine holiday.

John Milton

How-de-do?

L. B. P.

FIRST GROUP

mi (3) fa so so   so la so fa mi

"How - de - do and how - de - do and how - de - do to - day?

do re mi mi   mi fa mi re do

Come a - long, oh, come a - long for it's a hol - i - day."

SECOND GROUP

"Thank you, we are do - ing fine and wish for you the same.

We are com - ing, we are com - ing now to join your game."

16

How Sweet Is Our Singing

do (1)   *mi do ti re do so*

Oh, how sweet, how sweet is our sing - ing,

Oh, how sweet, how sweet is our song.

Clapping Game

L. B. P.

German Folk Tune

do   *fa re ti so mi do*

All to - geth - er here we go, Clap, clap, clap, clap, clap, clap!

fa re ti re do

Heads a - nod - ding, nod - ding so, Clap, clap, clap, clap, clap!

slower   *faster*

All stand up and turn a - round, Clap, clap, clap, clap, clap, clap!

slower   *faster*

Turn a - gain and then sit down, Clap, clap, clap, clap, clap!

Play this on melody instruments.

17

Playtime

Harry Hadley Schyde

1(do) 3 5 8 6 8 6 5

1. We like to sing, we like to dance,
2. Now we stand up, now we sit down;

We like to skip all a - round and to prance. We like to play,
Up a - gain, now we are whirl - ing a - round. Raise our hands high,

jump ev - 'ry way, We like to laugh and be hap - py each day.
point to the west, Clap our hands, one, two, three, sit down and rest.

Merry-Go-Round

Teacher sings.

Mer - ry - go - round, mer - ry - go - round, round and round and round.

You make up your "answer."

Rid - ing a - round, rid - ing a - round, round and round and round.

Merry-Go-Round

Dorothy W. Baruch[1]

Peter Dalton

I climbed up on the mer-ry-go-round, And it went round and round.

I climbed up on a big brown horse And it went up and down,

A-round and round and up and down, A-round and round and up and down.

I sat high up on a big brown horse And rode a-round on the

mer - ry - go - round, A - round and round and round. ·

Listen to and dramatize "Flying Birds (Merry-go-round rhythm)," Anderson. (Victor Rhythm Album One.)

[1]From *I Like Machinery*, published by Harper and Brothers. Used by permission of Dorothy W. Baruch.

Swing, swing,
Sing, sing,
Here's my throne, and I am a king!
Swing, sing,
Swing, sing,
Farewell, Earth, for I'm on the wing!

William Allingham

Up in a Swing

J. G. G.   June Goethe Garrels

do (1)

How would you like to go up in a swing? Up in a swing so   high?

O-ver the tree tops and chim-neys tall, Up in the blue, blue   sky?

Oh, it's fun when we're sail - ing high, Like   a   bird on   the   wing;

How would you like to come swing with me, Swing-ing 'way up in the   sky?

Listen to "Barcarolle," Rubinstein. (Victor Rhythm Album One.)

20

Oopsy Daisy Oh!

Louise Ayres Garnett

Yugoslavian Folk Tune

1 (do)   3   5

1. Go - ing up in a swing is a jol - ly thing;
2. Go - ing up makes a breeze in the tops of trees;

Oop - sy dai - sy oh! oop - sy dai - sy oh!
Oop - sy dai - sy oh! oop - sy dai - sy oh!

Com - ing down with a swoop near - ly loops a loop;
Com - ing down all the ground seems to turn a - round;

Oh, oop - sy dai - dai - sy, oop - sy dai - sy!
Oh, oop - sy dai - dai - sy, oop - sy dai - sy!

No - bod - y's la - zy, dai - sy oh! .
Ev - 'ry - thing's ha - zy, dai - sy oh!

Listen to "Waltz, Op. 39, No. 2," Brahms. (Victor Rhythm Album Two.)

Little Girl

Rope-jumping Chant

1. Lit-tle girl, lit-tle girl, Yes, ma'am! Did you go to town? Yes, ma'am!
2. Did you see my beau? Yes, ma'am! Did he buy me shoes? Yes, ma'am!
3. And some stock-ings, too? Yes, ma'am! Put him on the train? Yes, ma'am!

4. Did the big bell ring? Yes, ma'am! Which-a way did he go?

Choo-choo, all night long, choo-choo, all night long.

Strawberry Jam, Cream of Tartum

Rope-jumping Song

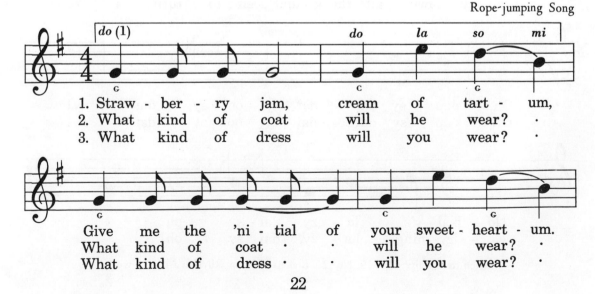

1. Straw - ber - ry jam, cream of tart - um,
2. What kind of coat will he wear?
3. What kind of dress will you wear?

Give me the 'ni - tial of your sweet - heart - um.
What kind of coat will he wear?
What kind of dress will you wear?

22

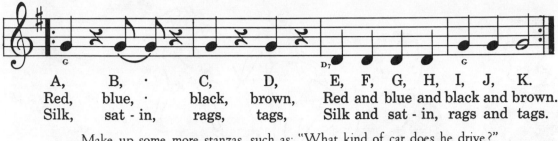

A, B, · C, D, E, F, G, H, I, J, K.
Red, blue, · black, brown, Red and blue and black and brown.
Silk, sat-in, rags, tags, Silk and sat-in, rags and tags.

Make up some more stanzas, such as: "What kind of car does he drive?"
"What kind of food does she eat?" etc.

Listen to "Gigue (Skipping Dance),"Corelli. (Victor Rhythm Album One.)

Whither, Little Path?

Translated by Alma Turechek

Czech Folk Song

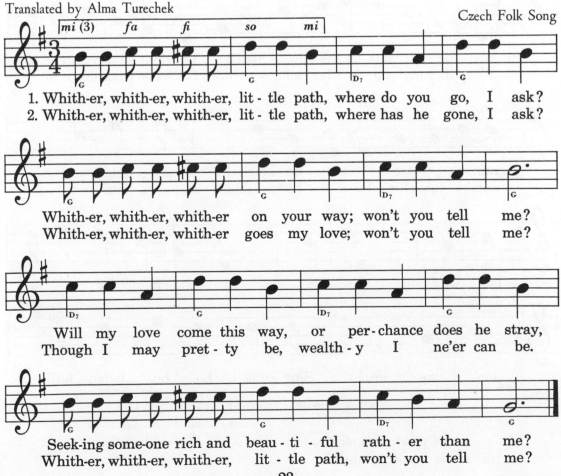

1. Whith-er, whith-er, whith-er, lit-tle path, where do you go, I ask?
2. Whith-er, whith-er, whith-er, lit-tle path, where has he gone, I ask?

Whith-er, whith-er, whith-er on your way; won't you tell me?
Whith-er, whith-er, whith-er goes my love; won't you tell me?

Will my love come this way, or per-chance does he stray,
Though I may pret-ty be, wealth-y I ne'er can be.

Seek-ing some-one rich and beau-ti-ful rath-er than me?
Whith-er, whith-er, whith-er, lit-tle path, won't you tell me?

Ho-Heigh-Ho

L. B. P.

so (5) do mi so la so fa re ti

1. We like to walk on the broad high-way, To tramp and tramp on a
2. We like high up in the hills to climb, To walk back down in

rain - y day. So it's ho - heigh - ho as a - long we go,
dou-ble-quick time. So it's ho - heigh - ho as a - long we go,

1, 2. On we go, on we go; It's ho - heigh - ho as a -

long we go, Sing - ing ho - ho, heigh - ho!

Listen to "March in F," Anderson. (Victor Rhythm Album One.)
Listen to "March," Gurlitt. (Victor Rhythm Album Two.) Listen for fa-
miliar tone patterns: *mi re | do so so so | do so do mi | re*, then the *octave* skip in
the middle section: *mi mi mi.*

24

Hare and Hounds

Christine Turner Curtis

Portuguese Singing Game

1. The hare is up on the hill-side, The hounds are wait-ing be-low;
2. The hare is speed-y and cun-ning, So do not slack-en your pace;

The horn will give us the sig-nal, And off the hunt-ers will go.
Up hill, and down by the mead-ow, The hounds will fol-low the chase.

1, 2. Oh, pay no heed to the weath-er, Nor fear the wind or rain;

We'll go a-hunt-ing to-geth-er A-cross the hills a-gain.

Listen to "Jagdlied (Hunting Song)," Schumann. (Victor Rhythm Album One.)

Crossing the Brook

Translated by Susanna Myers

Spanish Folk Song

mi (3)

1. Walk-ing in the coun-try Through a pleas-ant val-ley,
2. Search-ing in the riv-er, There a-mong the peb-bles,

He be-gan to whis-tle, I be-gan to sing, sing, sing,
I picked up a treas-ure pret-ty as my ring, ring, ring,

I be-gan to sing. He crossed a lit-tle riv-er and I
Pret-ty as my ring. A gold and sil-ver lock-et, such a

dropped my ring, ring, ring! 'Twas a pret-ty ring. He crossed a lit-tle
love-ly thing, thing, thing; Though I lost my ring. A gold and sil-ver

riv-er and I dropped my ring, ring, ring! 'Twas a pret-ty ring.
lock-et, such a love-ly thing, thing, thing; Though I lost my ring.

Just for Fun

Old Obadiah, he jumped in the fire.
The fire was so hot he jumped in the pot.
The pot was so black he jumped in a crack.
The crack was so shallow he jumped in the tallow.
The tallow was so soft he jumped in the loft.
The loft was so high he jumped to the sky.
The sky was so blue he jumped in the glue,
And there he was stuck, and we are stuck too.
How about you?

There Was a Man in Our Town

Folk Song

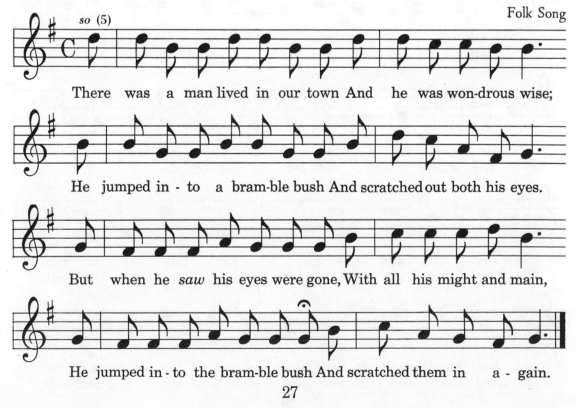

There was a man lived in our town And he was won-drous wise;

He jumped in-to a bram-ble bush And scratched out both his eyes.

But when he *saw* his eyes were gone, With all his might and main,

He jumped in-to the bram-ble bush And scratched them in a-gain.

27

Once a Lady Loved a Swine

Traditional

1. Once a la - dy loved a swine, "Hon - ey," said she,
2. "I'll build thee a sil - ver sty, Hon - ey," said she,

"Dar - ling pig, will you be mine?" "Oink," said he.
"Dar - ling pig, will you be mine?" "Oink," said he.

Too-Ril-Te-Too

Traditional

1. Oh, Too - ril - te - too was a bon - ny cock rob - in,
2. Oh, Too - ril - te - too was so proud of his tail,

He tied up his tail with a piece of blue bob - bin.
To show it off bet - ter, he stood on a rail.

His tail was the size of the tail of a flea,
A hun - gry old cat crept up o - ver the wall,

But he thought it was fine as a tail could be.
And she ate up poor Too - ril - te - too, tail and all.

28

The Sow with the Measles

New England Traditional

so (5)

1, 2, 3. The old sow took the mea-sles, and she died in the spring;

What did we do with the old sow's hide?
What did we do with the old sow's hair?
What did we do with the old sow's squeal?

Made a good sad-dle for an-y-one to ride;
Made e-nough sat-in for an-y-one to wear;
Some-thing we knew she had, but we could-n't feel;

Sad-dle or wag-on seat — an-y such thing! The old
Sat-in or broad-cloth — an-y such thing! The old
Could-n't use that for an-y old thing! The old

1, 2, 3. sow took the mea-sles, and she died in the spring.

29

Frog Went A-Courtin'

Mississippi Version

1. A frog went a-court-in', he did ride, uh, huh!
2. He rode up to Miss Mous-ie's door, uh, huh!

A frog went a-court-in', he did ride
He rode up to Miss Mous-ie's door, A

Sword and pis-tol by his side, uh, huh!
place he'd nev-er been be-fore, uh, huh!

3. Miss Mousie she came tripping down, uh, huh!
   In a brand new hat and her Sunday gown, uh, huh!

4. Mister Frog took Mousie on his knee, uh, huh!
   And said, "Miss Mousie, won't you marry me, uh, huh?"

5. "Oh, not without Uncle Rat's consent, uh, huh!
   Could I think of marrying the President, uh, huh!"

6. Uncle Rat right then came riding home, uh, huh!
   Said, "Who's come here while I was gone, uh, huh?"

7. "A nice young man of eighty-three, uh, huh!
   Who says he wants to marry me, uh, huh!"

8. Old Rat he laughed and shook his fat sides, uh, huh!
   To think his niece would be a bride, uh, huh!

9. Oh, where will the wedding supper be, uh, huh?
   'Way down yonder in a hollow tree, uh, huh!

10. The first to come was a big white moth, uh, huh!
    And around her neck was a table cloth, uh, huh!

11. The next to come was an old red hen, uh, huh!
    Tuning up her fiddle to please the men, uh, huh!

12. Oh, next to come was a black old flea, uh, huh!
   Strumming a banjo on his knee, uh, huh!

13. Next to come was brown muley cow, uh, huh!
   She tried to dance but didn't know how, uh, huh!

14. The next to come was a betsy bug, uh, huh!
   Who brought lemonade in a little brown jug, uh, huh!

15. And then there came our old gray cat, uh, huh!
   Who said, "I'll put an end to that, uh, huh!"

16. Miss Mousie scampered up the wall, uh, huh!
   Her right foot slipped and she got a bad fall, uh, huh!

17. Mister Frog swam out into the lake, uh, huh!
   And got swallowed up by a long green snake, uh, huh!

18. Miss Mousie sat and cried and cried, uh, huh!
   Because her husband had gone and died, uh, huh!

The Bee and the Pup

Traditional

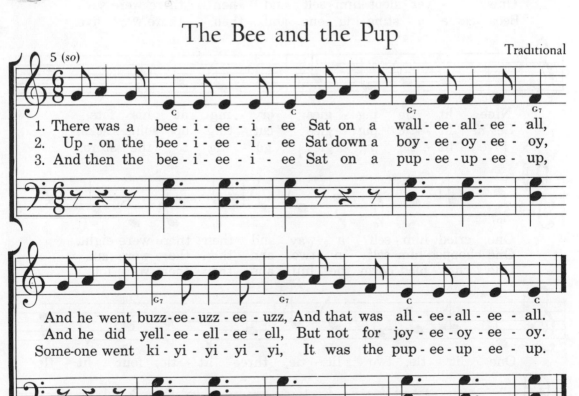

1. There was a bee-i-ee-i-ee Sat on a wall-ee-all-ee-all,
2. Up-on the bee-i-ee-i-ee Sat down a boy-ee-oy-ee-oy,
3. And then the bee-i-ee-i-ee Sat on a pup-ee-up-ee-up,

And he went buzz-ee-uzz-ee-uzz, And that was all-ee-all-ee-all.
And he did yell-ee-ell-ee-ell, But not for joy-ee-oy-ee-oy.
Some-one went ki-yi-yi-yi-yi, It was the pup-ee-up-ee-up.

One of you play this on the piano while others play the tune on melody instruments.

31

Ten Little Piggies

Old Song

so (5) do (1)

1. Ten lit - tle pig - gies go - ing out to dine,
2. Eight lit - tle pig - gies slept un - til e - lev'n,
3. Six lit - tle pig - gies play - ing with a hive,

One choked his lit - tle self and then there were nine.
One o - ver - slept him - self and then there were sev'n.
Bees came a - sting - ing one and then there were five.

Nine lit - tle pig - gies cry - ing at his fate,
Sev'n lit - tle pig - gies cut - ting up some sticks,
Five lit - tle pig - gies go - ing to the store,

One cried him - self a - way and then there were eight.
One chopped him - self in two and then there were six.
One tum - bled down the hill and then there were four.

CHORUS

One lit - tle, two lit - tle, three lit - tle, four lit - tle,

five lit - tle pig - gy - wigs; Six lit - tle, sev'n lit - tle,

32

eight lit-tle, nine lit-tle, ten lit-tle pig-gy-wigs.

4. Four little piggies going out to sea,
Big Whale swallowed one
And then there were three;
Three little piggies walking in the zoo,
Big Bear hugged one
And then there were two.

5. Two little piggies sitting in the sun,
One got frizzled up
And then there was one;
One little piggie living all alone,
He got married
And then there were none.

Hot Dog

Camp Song

I have a little puppy, He has a stubby tail. He isn't very chubby,

He's skinny as a rail. He'll always be a puppy, He'll never be a hound.

They sell him at the butcher shop   For twenty cents a pound.

Bow - wow - wow - wow - wow - wow - wow - wow! Hot   dog!

33

Grumbling Joe

Traditional

Ronald Avery

mi   *la*

gm   D7   gm   D7

1. He did-n't like mut-ton, he did-n't like bread,
2. He did-n't like les-sons, he did-n't like play,
3. His grum-bling at length did be-come such a bore

gm   D7   gm   D7

He did-n't like an-y-thing an-y-one said;
He did-n't like danc-ing, he nev-er was gay;
His fa-ther de-clared he should grum-ble no more,

gm   D7   gm   D7

He did-n't like ris-ing or go-ing to bed,
He did-n't like or-ders, he'd nev-er o-bey,
So bor-rowed a switch from his neigh-bor next door,

gm   gm   D7   D7   gm   gm

Did-n't Grum-bling, Grum - bling Joe.
Would-n't Grum-bling, Grum - bling Joe.
All for Grum-bling, Grum - bling Joe.

gm   D7   gm

Poor · Joe. ·

Singing at Work

I've Been Workin' on the Railroad

do (1)   Traditional

I've been work-in' on the rail - road   All   the live-long   day.

I've been work-in' on the rail - road   To pass the time a - way.

re di re

Can't you hear the whis-tle blow-ing? Rise up so ear-ly in the morn.

Can't you hear the cap-tain shout - ing: "Di - nah, blow your horn!"

Leave Her, Johnny

SOLO
1 (do)

CHORUS

Sea Chantey
mi so

1. I · thought I heard the · skip-per say, Leave her, John-ny, leave her!
2. The work was hard, the voyage was long, Leave her, John-ny, leave her!

SOLO
mi la

CHORUS

To - mor-row you will   get your pay, It's time for us to   leave her.
The seas were high, the gales were strong, It's time for us to   leave her.

3. The food was bad, the wages low,
   Leave her, Johnny, leave her!
   But now ashore again we'll go,
   It's time for us to leave her.

4. The sails are furled, our work is done,
   Leave her, Johnny, leave her!
   And now on shore, we'll have our fun,
   It's time for us to leave her.

Listen to "Overture to 'The Flying Dutchman'," Wagner. (Columbia record.)

36

Haul on the Bowlin'

Sea Chantey

SOLO

1. Haul on the bow-lin', The fore and main-top bow-lin',
2. Haul on the bow-lin', The skip-per he's a-growl-ing,
3. Haul on the bow-lin', To Lon-don we are go-ing,

CHORUS

Haul on the bow-lin', the bow-lin' haul!

Blow, Boys, Blow

Sea Chantey

SOLO

1. A Yan-kee ship sailed down the riv-er. Blow, boys, blow.
2. How do you know she's a Yan-kee Clip-per? Blow, boys, blow

SOLO

Her mast did bend, her sails did shiv-er. Blow, my jol-ly boys, blow.
The Stars and Stripes float out a-bove her. Blow, my jol-ly boys, blow.

3. The sails were old, her sides were rotten.
   Blow, boys, blow.
   His charts the skipper had forgotten.
   Blow, my jolly boys, blow.

4. The men were anything but frisky.
   Blow, boys, blow.
   They'd never crossed the Bay of Biscay.
   Blow, my jolly boys, blow.

5. What do you think they had for dinner?
   Blow, boys, blow.
   'Twas water soup, but slightly thinner.
   Blow, my jolly boys, blow.

6. She sailed away for London city.
   Blow, boys, blow.
   She never got there, what a pity.
   Blow, my jolly boys, blow.

Good-By, Old Paint

Cowboy Song

la (6) so la do la la so mi re do

1. Good - by, old Paint, I'm a - leav - ing Chey - enne, My
2. Good - by, old Paint, I'm a - leav - ing Chey - enne, I'm
3. Good - by, old Paint, I'm a - leav - ing Chey - enne, Go

foot in the stir - rup, my po - ny won't stan'; · I'm a
rid - ing old Paint and a - lead - ing old Fan; · Good ·
hitch up your hors - es and give them some hay, · And ·

leav - ing Chey - enne an' I'm off to Mon - tan'. ·
by, lit - tle An - nie, I'm off to Mon - tan'. ·
seat your - self by me as long as you stay. ·

CHORUS

Good - by, old Paint, I'm a - leav - ing Chey - enne.

38

My Home's in Montana

Paraphrase from "Singing Cowboy"

Cowboy Song

1. My home's in Mon - ta - na, I wear a ban - dan - na; My
2. When val - leys are dust - y, My po - ny is trust - y; He
3. When far from the ranch - es, I chop the pine branch - es To

spurs are of sil - ver, My po - ny is gray. When
lopes through the bliz - zard, The snow in his ears. The
heap on my camp - fire As day - light grows pale; When

rid - ing the rang - es My luck nev - er chang - es: With
cat - tle may scat - ter, But what does it mat - ter! My
I have par - tak - en Of beans and of ba - con, I

foot in the stir - rup I'll gal - lop a - way.
rope is a hal - ter For pig - head - ed steers.
whis - tle a mer - ry Old song of the trail.

Night Herding Song

Cowboy Song

1. Oh say, lit - tle do - gies, quit rov - ing a - round,
2. Oh, lay down, my do - gies, quit sift - ing a - round,

You've wan - dered and tram - pled all o - ver the ground.
Just stretch a - way out on the big, o - pen ground.

Oh, graze a - long, do - gies, and move kind - a slow,
My horse is leg - wea - ry and I'm aw - ful tired,

And don't be for - ev - er so much on the go,
If you get a - way, then I'll sure - ly be fired.

Move slow, lit-tle do-gies, move slow. Hi - o, hi - o, hi - o.
Oh, lay down, my do-gies, lay down. Hi - o, hi - o, hi - o.

With My Bow

Copper Eskimo Song

With my bow I tried to kill, tried to kill a car - i - bou,

40

With my bow I tried to kill, tried to kill a car-i-bou.

Fly-ing ar-row, fly-ing ar-row caught one stamp-ing on the ground,

Fly-ing ar-row, fly-ing ar-row brought it down, brought it down.

In the Ice

Copper Eskimo Song

do (1)

In the ice, in the snow, yi-i-i-i, ya-ya-ya, Quick-ly with my

spear I'll strike; At the beard-ed seal I'll strike, When up to their

ritard

holes they come, In the ice, in the snow, yi-i-i-i, ya-ya-ya.

41

Salad Greens

Translated by Cecil Cowdrey

French Folk Song

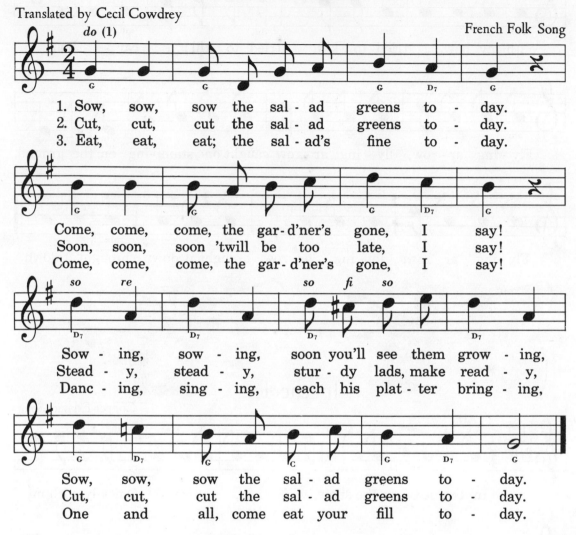

1. Sow, sow, sow the sal-ad greens to-day.
2. Cut, cut, cut the sal-ad greens to-day.
3. Eat, eat, eat; the sal-ad's fine to-day.

Come, come, come, the gar-d'ner's gone, I say!
Soon, soon, soon 'twill be too late, I say!
Come, come, come, the gar-d'ner's gone, I say!

Sow - ing, sow - ing, soon you'll see them grow - ing,
Stead - y, stead - y, stur - dy lads, make read - y,
Danc - ing, sing - ing, each his plat - ter bring - ing,

Sow, sow, sow the sal-ad greens to-day.
Cut, cut, cut the sal-ad greens to-day.
One and all, come eat your fill to-day.

Annie Goes to the Cabbage Patch

Translated

Bohemian Singing Game

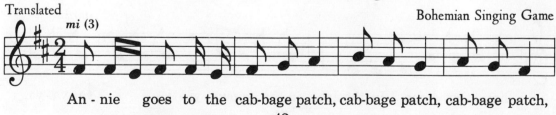

An - nie goes to the cab-bage patch, cab-bage patch, cab-bage patch,

42

Look-ing for leaves that are fresh and green to feed her rab-bits white.

so so la so re re re so so la so mi mi mi

John-ny sees her, ha, ha, ha! Now I'll catch you, tra la la!

Nay, nay, nay, go a-way! I'll not dance with you to-day!

San Sereni

Translated by Cecil Cowdrey

Mexican Folk Song

5 (*so*)   5 #4 5

1. San Se-re-ni, this is not the time for nap-ping;
2. San Se-re-ni, it is time that you were wak-ing;
3. San Se-re-ni, don't you hear the noise a-sound-ing?

Loud-ly be-low I hear the cob-blers
Gai-ly be-low I hear the bak-ers
Loud-ly be-low The car-pen-ters are

tap-ping, tap-ping, tap-ping, tap-ping so.
bak-ing, bak-ing, bak-ing, bak-ing so.
pound-ing, pound-ing, pound-ing, pound-ing so.

43

The Little Tailor

Eleanor Farjeon[1]

Henry M. Halvorson

1. I saw a lit-tle Tai-lor sit-ting stitch, stitch, stitch-ing
2. His silk · and his cot-ton he was thread, thread, thread-ing
3. He hummed as he worked a mer-ry dit, dit, dit-ty:

Cross - leg-ged on the floor of his kitch, kitch, kitch-en.
For a gown · and a coat for a wed, wed, wed-ding.
"The · bride · is as plump as she's pret, pret, pret-ty.

His thumbs and his fin-gers were so nim, nim, nim-ble
His nee-dle flew as swift · as a swal, swal, swal-low,
I would-n't have her tall - er or short, short, short-er,

With his wax and his scis-sors and his thim, thim, thim-ble.
And his spools and his reels · had to fol, fol, fol-low.
She can laugh like the fall - ing of wat, wat, wa-ter.

4. She can put a cherry pie togeth, geth, gether,
   She can dance as light as a feath, feath, feather,
   She can sing as sweet as a fid, fid, fiddle,
   And she's only twenty inches round the mid, mid, middle."

5. The happy little Tailor went on stitch, stitch, stitching
   The black and the white in his kitch, kitch, kitchen.
   He will wear the black one, she will wear the white one,
   And the knot the Parson ties will be a tight, tight, tight one.

[1]From *Cherrystones*, copyright 1942 by Eleanor Farjeon. Reprinted by permission of the Author and Michael Joseph, Ltd.

44

Singing Games

The Noble Duke of York

so (5) do (1)

Traditional

The no-ble Duke of York, He had ten thou-sand men, He
(All seated.)

led them up the hill, Then led them down a-gain. And
(All stand.) *(All sit down.)*

when they're up, they're up, And when they're down, they're down; But
(All stand.) *(All sit.)*

when they're in be-tween, They're nei-ther up nor down.
(All half stand.) *(Leap up, clap hands above heads, and sit down.)*

45

Four in a Boat

1 (do)

Singing Game

1. Four in a boat and the tide rolls high,
2. Get me a pret - ty one, stay all day,
3. Eight in a boat and it won't go round,

Four in a boat and the tide rolls high,
Get me a pret - ty one, stay all day,
Eight in a boat and it won't go round,

Get you a pret - ty one bye and bye,
We don't care what the oth - ers say,
Swing that pret - ty one you've just found,

Get you a pret - ty one bye and bye.
We don't care what the oth - ers say.
Swing that pret - ty one you've just found.

Form a single circle, hands joined, facing center. Four boys in center (inner circle) hands joined, facing outer circle. *Stanza 1.* Outer circle skips or walks around to the left. Inner circle does the same in the opposite direction. *Stanza 2.* All drop hands and both circles move in the same direction. Each boy in center chooses a girl in the outer circle and walks beside her until the end of the stanza. *Stanza 3.* Each boy in the center pulls his partner into the inner circle. Both circles join hands and move in opposite directions, as in the first stanza. They pretend that the boat won't go around until "Swing that pretty one," when each boy in the inner circle swings his partner, hands joined, and then leaves her in the center. The song is repeated with girls in the center.

46

Marching 'Round the Levee

American Singing Game

1. We're march-ing 'round the lev - ee, We're march-ing 'round the lev - ee,
   Circle of alternate boys and girls walk to the right. Boy and girl in center.

2. Go in and out the win-dow, Go in and out the win-dow,
   Boy and girl in center weave in and out windows and look for partners.

We're march-ing 'round the lev - ee, For we have gained the day.
Circle stands. Lifted arms form windows.

Go in and out the win-dow, As we have done be - fore.

3. Go forth and face your partner, *Center boy and girl stand before partners.*
   For we have gained the day.

4. I kneel before my partner, *Kneel before partners.*
   For we have gained the day.

5. And now I'll take my partner, *Stand and take partners by the hand.*
   For we have gained the day.

6. Now off we go to London, *Skip with partners inside the circle. Partners chosen*
   For we have gained the day. *remain in circle and the game begins over again.*

I'll Give to You a Paper of Pins

Traditional Song

He 1. "I'll give to you a pa-per of pins, And that's the way my love be-gins, If you will mar-ry me, me, me, If you will mar-ry me."

She 2. "I'll not ac-cept your pa-per of pins, If that's the way your love be-gins, And I'll not mar-ry you, you, you, For I'll not mar-ry you."

He 3. "I'll give to you a dress · of red All bound · round with gold-en thread, If you will mar-ry me, me, me, If you will mar-ry me."

She 4. "I'll not ac-cept your dress · of red All bound · round with gold-en thread, And I'll not mar-ry you, you, you, For I'll not mar-ry you."

He 5. "I'll give to you the key to my heart,
That you and I may never part,
If you will marry me, me, me,
If you will marry me."

She 6. "I will accept the key to your heart,
That you and I may never part,
And I will marry you, you, you,
And I will marry you."

48

Dog Tick

Texas Singing Game

Center player sings.

1. "Dog tick, dog tick, Dog tick bit - in' me!"
2. "Red ant, black ant, Big ant bit - in' me!"
3. "Spi - der, spi - der, Spi - der bit - in' me!"

Circle players sing.

1, 2, 3, 4, 5. "Don't care, don't care! Can't get out · of here!"

4. "Bumblebee, bumblebee,   5. "Grandma, grandma,
   Bumblebee stingin' me!"   Grandma callin' me!"

Form a circle and join hands around a center player. Center player sings the first line while trying to get out of the circle. Circle players answer with "Don't care," etc. When center player finally breaks through, the others chase and catch him.

Choose Your Rock Candy

Singing Game

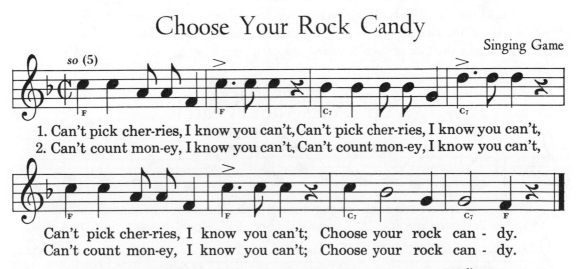

1. Can't pick cher-ries, I know you can't, Can't pick cher-ries, I know you can't,
2. Can't count mon-ey, I know you can't, Can't count mon-ey, I know you can't,

Can't pick cher-ries, I know you can't; Choose your rock can - dy.
Can't count mon-ey, I know you can't; Choose your rock can - dy.

Join hands and form a circle. Choose a player for the center. Walk a-round him while singing. Center player tries to act out the words for each stanza. He then chooses someone to take his place, and the game is repeat-ed. Make up other stanzas for this song.

49

Rise You Up, My True Love

Mississippi Singing Game

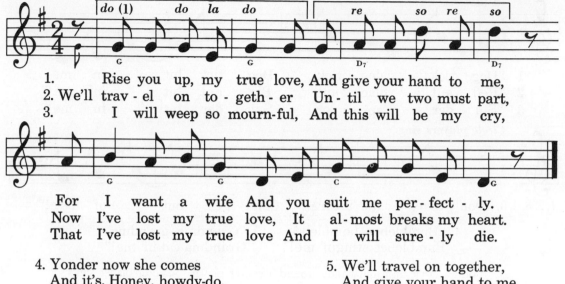

1.   Rise you up, my true love, And give your hand to me,
2. We'll trav - el on to - geth - er Un - til we two must part,
3.   I will weep so mourn-ful, And this will be my cry,

For I want a wife And you suit me per - fect - ly.
Now I've lost my true love, It al-most breaks my heart.
That I've lost my true love And I will sure - ly die.

4. Yonder now she comes
    And it's, Honey, howdy-do,
    And how have you been
    Since the time I last saw you?

5. We'll travel on together,
    And give your hand to me,
    For I want a wife
    And you suit me perfectly.

Form two lines, with partners facing. Head couple joins hands and skips down between the lines. At "Until we two must part" the boy skips behind the line of girls, the girl behind the line of boys. At "Yonder now she comes" the two join hands and skip between the lines again. They take position at the foot of each line, and the game begins again with a new head couple.

Pop! Goes the Weasel

Singing Game

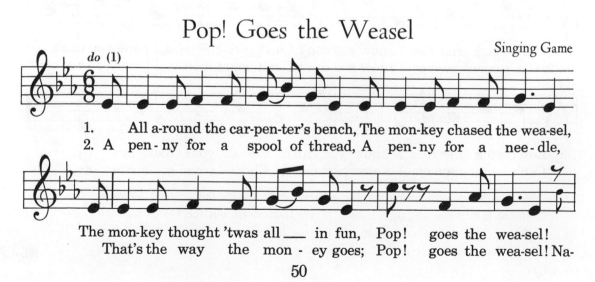

1.   All a-round the car-pen-ter's bench, The mon-key chased the wea-sel,
2. A pen - ny for a spool of thread, A pen-ny for a nee - dle,

The mon-key thought 'twas all __ in fun, Pop! goes the wea-sel!
That's the way the mon - ey goes; Pop! goes the wea-sel! Na-

I've no time to   wait or sigh, No pa-tience to wait till   by and by;
po-leon's got the whoop-ing cough, Vic-to - ria's got the   mea - sles;

Kiss me quick, I'm   off, good-by!   Pop!   goes the   wea - sel!
That's the way the   mon - ey goes;   Pop!   goes the   wea - sel!

The Pawpaw Patch

Singing Game

do (1)   so   mi   do

1. Where, oh, where is   dear · lit-tle Ma - ry? Where, oh, where is
2. Come on, boys, and let's · go · find her, Come on, boys, and
3. Scoop-ing up paw-paws, put them in a   bas-ket, Scoop-ing up paw-paws,

re   ti   so

dear · lit-tle Ma - ry? Where, oh, where is   dear · lit-tle Ma - ry?
let's · go · find her, Come · on, boys, and let's · go · find her,
put them in a   bas - ket, Scoop-ing up paw-paws, put them in a   bas - ket,

1, 2, 3. 'Way down yon-der in the paw-paw patch.

Game directions for "The Pawpaw Patch" are in your
teacher's book.

51

Miss Jenny-O-Jones

Singing Game

so (5)   *so*   *mi*   *do*

Knock, knock, knock!   We've come · to see · Miss Jen-ny - o - Jones,
Miss Jen-ny - o - Jones is chop-ping the wood,
We're ver - y sor-ry to hear · of it,

re   *ti*   *so*

Miss   Jen - ny - o - Jones,   Miss   Jen - ny - o - Jones,
Is   chop - ping the wood,   is   chop - ping the wood,
To   hear · of it,   to   hear · of it,

We've   come   to   see · Miss   Jen - ny - o - Jones,
Miss   Jen - ny - o - Jones · is   chop - ping the wood,
We're   ver - y   sor - ry to   hear · of it,

1, 2   **3**

And   how   is   she · to - day? ·
And   can't   see   you · to - day. ·
We'll   call   an - oth - er   day.

You may add as many stanzas as you like, such as: washing and ironing
clothes, sweeping and dusting, etc.

52

The Bridge of Avignon

French Folk Song

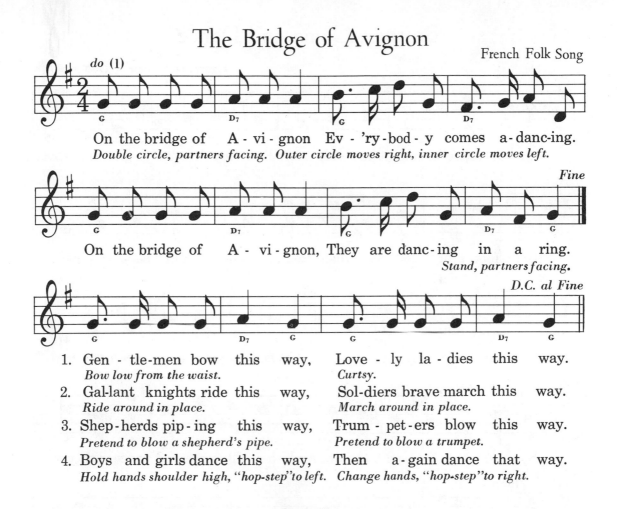

On the bridge of A - vi - gnon Ev - 'ry - bod - y comes a - danc-ing.
Double circle, partners facing. Outer circle moves right, inner circle moves left.

On the bridge of A - vi - gnon, They are danc-ing in a ring.
Stand, partners facing.

1. Gen - tle-men bow this way,   Love - ly la - dies this way.
   Bow low from the waist.   *Curtsy.*
2. Gal-lant knights ride this way,   Sol-diers brave march this way.
   Ride around in place.   *March around in place.*
3. Shep - herds pip - ing this way,   Trum - pet-ers blow this way.
   Pretend to blow a shepherd's pipe.   *Pretend to blow a trumpet.*
4. Boys and girls dance this way,   Then a - gain dance that way.
   Hold hands shoulder high, "hop-step" to left.   *Change hands, "hop-step" to right.*

Brother, Come and Dance

GRETEL

"Hansel and Gretel", Humperdinck

Broth - er, come and dance with me, Both my hands I give to thee;

Right foot first, left foot then, Round a - bout and back a - gain.

HANSEL

I would dance, but don't know how, When to step and when to bow;

Show me what I ought to do And then I'll come and dance with you.

BOTH

Let your feet go tap, tap, tap, Let your hands go clap, clap, clap;
Let your head go nick, nick, nick, Let your fin - gers click, click, click;

Right foot first, left foot then, Round a - bout and back a - gain.
Right foot first, left foot then, Round a - bout and back a - gain.

Listen to "Hansel and Gretel," Humperdinck. (Victor Listening Album Four.)

54

The Buffalo Head Dance

Plains Indians' Song

Yay · · yay · wee yay yah wee yay yah hah
Go hunt the buf-fa-lo that roam on the prai-rie,

Yay · · yay · wee yay yah wee yay yah hah
Go hunt the buf-fa-lo that roam on the prai-rie,

Yay · · yay · wee yay yah wee yay yah hah
Great shag-gy buf-fa-lo that graze on the prai-rie,

Wee yay hay wee yay hay hah yah
May there be buf-fa-lo man-y,

Wee yay hay wee yay hay ah yay hah.
May there be buf-fa-lo graz-ing there.

Listen to "Shawnee Indian Hunting Dance," Skilton. (Victor Indian Album for Elementary Grades.)

The Land of the Dutch, Dutch, Dutch

Unknown

Paul Forde

A - way 'way off 'cross the seas and such, Lies the

Face your partners, lock elbows and swing "step-hop" as if wearing wooden shoes.

lit-tle flat land of the Dutch, Dutch, Dutch! Where the wind-mills' arms go

Partners face with outstretched arms, imitate windmills.

round, round, round, And sing to the cows with a creak-y sound. Where

Imitate

storks live up in the chim - ney top, And wood - en shoes pound

stork standing on one foot. *Stand still.*

plop, plop, plop! Where milk cans shine in the shin - i - est way, And the

Stamp. *Boys shine milk cans.*

56

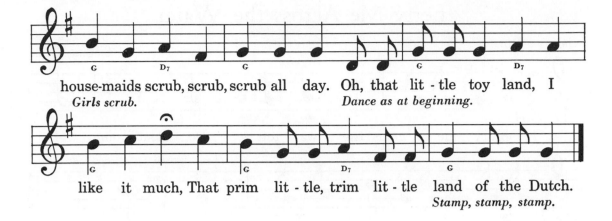

house-maids scrub, scrub, scrub all day. Oh, that lit - tle toy land, I

Girls scrub.   *Dance as at beginning.*

like it much, That prim lit - tle, trim lit - tle land of the Dutch.

Stamp, stamp, stamp.

Come, Boys and Girls

Translated   Norwegian Folk Game

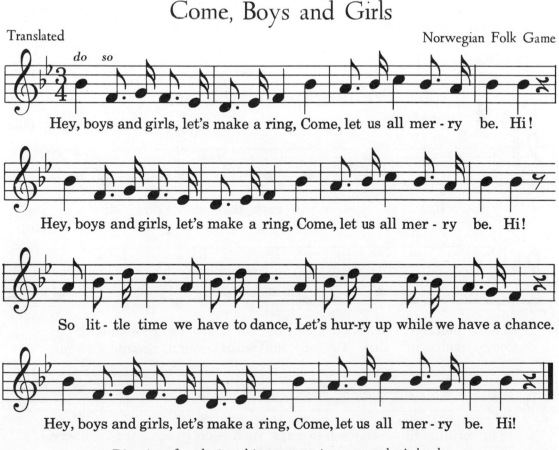

Hey, boys and girls, let's make a ring, Come, let us all mer - ry be. Hi!

Hey, boys and girls, let's make a ring, Come, let us all mer - ry be. Hi!

So lit - tle time we have to dance, Let's hur-ry up while we have a chance.

Hey, boys and girls, let's make a ring, Come, let us all mer - ry be. Hi!

Directions for playing this game are in your teacher's book.

Ferry Me Across the Water

Christina Rossetti

Singing Game

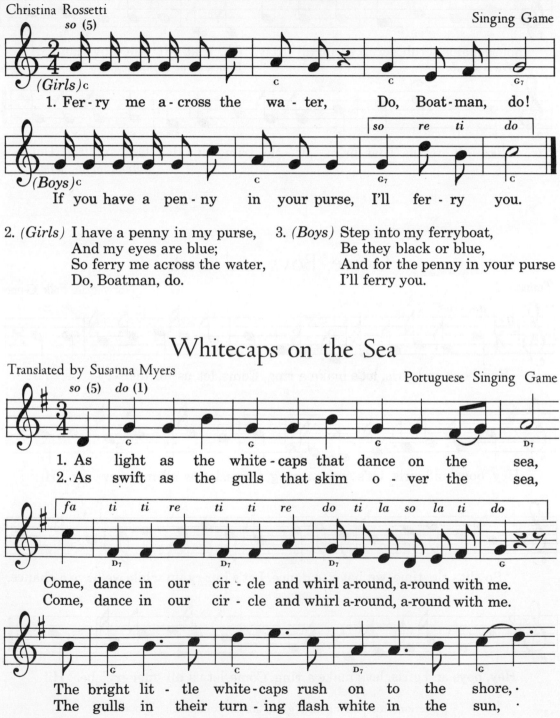

so (5)

(Girls) c   c   c   G₇

1. Fer-ry me a-cross the wa-ter, Do, Boat-man, do!

so re ti do

(Boys) c   c   G₇   c

If you have a pen-ny in your purse, I'll fer-ry you.

2. *(Girls)* I have a penny in my purse,
And my eyes are blue;
So ferry me across the water,
Do, Boatman, do.

3. *(Boys)* Step into my ferryboat,
Be they black or blue,
And for the penny in your purse
I'll ferry you.

Whitecaps on the Sea

Translated by Susanna Myers

Portuguese Singing Game

so (5)   do (1)

G   G   G   D₇

1. As light as the white-caps that dance on the sea,
2. As swift as the gulls that skim o-ver the sea,

fa ti ti re ti ti re do ti la so la ti do

D₇   D₇   D₇   G

Come, dance in our cir-cle and whirl a-round, a-round with me.
Come, dance in our cir-cle and whirl a-round, a-round with me.

G   C   D₇   G

The bright lit-tle white-caps rush on to the shore,
The gulls in their turn-ing flash white in the sun,

58

So, whirl-ing and turn-ing, we cir-cle round and round once more.
So, whirl-ing and cir-cling, come, dance to-geth-er, ev-'ry-one.

Directions for playing this game are in your teacher's book.

The Polka

Christine Turner Curtis

Russian Folk Tune

la fa re fa fa mi mi

1. Step, step, step, hop, step, step, step, hop, This is called the pol-ka dance.
2. Mer-ry pol-kas, mer-ry pol-kas Rus-sian peo-ple love to dance.
3. From the farm-yard, from the farm-yard Pol-kas sound on sum-mer nights.

Step, step, step, hop with a part-ner, All move clock-wise, smile and glance.
Three steps for-ward, three steps for-ward, Then a kind of hop and prance.
In the mead-ows, in the mead-ows Fire-flies hang their yel-low lights.

Stamp, stamp, heel and toe, Then go on with pol-ka slow;
Bal-a-lai-kas cry, Cheeks grow red, and sash-es fly.
Three steps, then a hop, On they dance and can-not stop.

Stamp, stamp, heel and toe, And re-peat the dance just so.
Girls wear crim-son boots, Boys wear blous-es with their suits.
Day breaks on the hill, Yet the crowds are danc-ing still.

Play this on melody instruments.

Here Come Three Sailors

English Singing Game

so (5)   *do* (1)

1. Here come three sail-ors, three by three, To
2. Oh, sleep, sleep, daugh-ter, do not wake, Here
3. Here come three sol-diers, three by three, To
4. Oh, sleep, sleep, daugh-ter, do not wake, Here

court your daugh-ter, a fair la-dy   Can we have a lodg-ing
are three sail-ors we can-not take.   We have not a lodg-ing
court your daugh-ter, a fair la-dy.   Can we have a lodg-ing
are three sol-diers we can-not take.   We have not a lodg-ing

here, here, here,   Can we have a lodg-ing here?
here, here, here,   We have not a lodg-ing here.
here, here, here,   Can we have a lodg-ing here?
here, here, here,   We have not a lodg-ing here.

5. Here come three kings, three by three,
   To court your daughter, a fair lady.
   Can we have a lodging here, here, here,
   Can we have a lodging here?

6. Oh, wake, daughter, wake and do not sleep,
   Here are three kings whom we can take.
   You may have a lodging here, here, here,
   You may have a lodging here.

7. Here's my daughter safe and sound,
   And in her pocket a hundred pound.
   Here upon her finger a gay gold ring,
   She is fit to walk with a king.

8. Take back your daughter safe and sound,
   Take from her pocket the hundred pound,
   Keep upon her finger the gay gold ring,
   She's not fit to walk with a king.

Directions for playing the games "Here Come Three Sailors," and "Three Pirates" are in your teacher's book.

60

Three Pirates

English Ballad

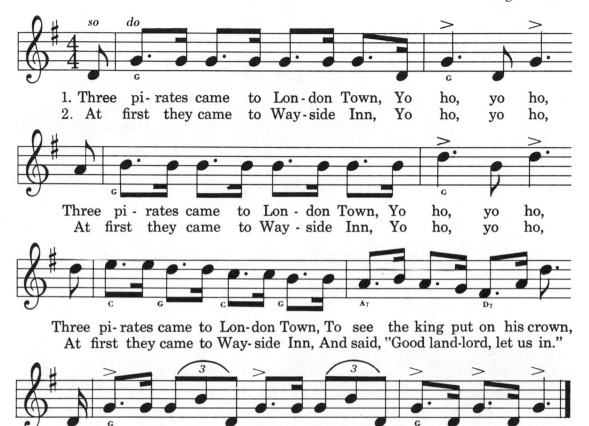

1. Three pi-rates came to Lon-don Town, Yo ho, yo ho,
2. At first they came to Way-side Inn, Yo ho, yo ho,

Three pi-rates came to Lon-don Town, Yo ho, yo ho,
At first they came to Way-side Inn, Yo ho, yo ho,

Three pi-rates came to Lon-don Town, To see the king put on his crown,
At first they came to Way-side Inn, And said, "Good land-lord, let us in."

1-8. Yo ho, you lub-bers, yo ho, you lub-bers, Yo ho, yo ho, yo ho!

3. Oh landlord, have you hoards of gold,
    Yo ho, yo ho,   *(repeat)*
Oh landlord, have you hoards of gold,
Enough to fill the after hold?

4. Oh yes, sir, I have hoards of gold,
    Yo ho, yo ho,   *(repeat)*
Oh yes, sir, I have hoards of gold,
Enough to fill the after hold.

5. Oh landlord, have you a daughter fair,
    Yo ho, yo ho,   *(repeat)*
Oh landlord, have you a daughter fair,
With laughing eyes and curly hair?

6. Oh yes, sir, I've a daughter fair,
    Yo ho, yo ho,   *(repeat)*
Oh yes, sir, I've a daughter fair,
With laughing eyes and curly hair.

7. Oh landlord, will she marry me,
    Yo ho, yo ho,   *(repeat)*
Oh landlord, will she marry me,
And sail with me across the sea?

8. Oh yes, sir, she will marry thee,
    Yo ho, yo ho,   *(repeat)*
Oh yes, sir, she will marry thee,
And sail with thee across the sea.

Home
and Family

My mother's hands are cool and fair,
They can do anything.

When I was small and could not sleep,
She used to come to me,
And with my cheek upon her hand
How sure my rest would be.

Anna Hempstead Branch

My Mother's Songs

L. B. P.   Walter Evans

1. I have a moth-er who sings to me,
2. I have a moth-er who sings to me,
3. I have a moth-er who sings to me

Of the bright white moon and the shin-ing stars,
Of · tall bell tow'rs reach-ing for the skies,
With · love-ly words and a lilt-ing rhyme,

Of sail-ors and pi-rates and bold Jack Tars,
Of peo-ple and chil-dren of ev-'ry size,
And quick-ened with glad-ness my heart beats time,

And all of the folk · who sail the seas.
And all of the things · I'd like to see.
For I have a moth-er who sings to me.

Home, Sweet Home

John Howard Payne

Henry Rowley Bishop

1. 'Mid pleas-ures and pal - a - ces though we may roam,
2. How sweet 'tis to sit 'neath a fond · fa-ther's smile,

Be it ev - er so hum-ble, there's no · place like home.
And the cares of a moth-er to soothe · and be - guile;

A charm from the skies seems to hal - low us there,
Let oth - ers de - light 'mid new pleas - ures to roam,

Which, seek through the world, is not met · with else - where.
But give me, oh, give me the pleas - ures of home.

Home, home, · sweet, sweet home!
Home, home, · sweet, sweet home!

There's no place like home, · there's no · place like. home.
There's no place like home, · there's no · place like home.

Hush, Little Baby

Traditional

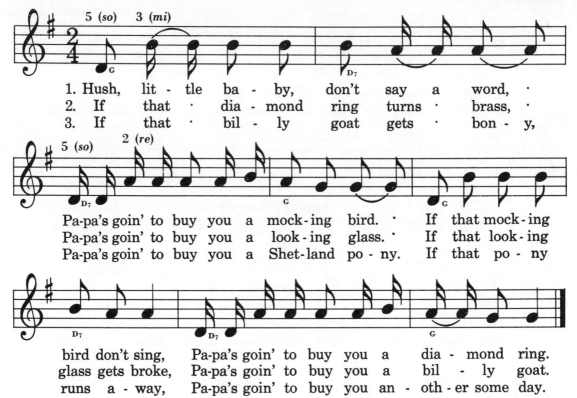

1. Hush, lit - tle ba - by, don't say a word, ·
2. If that · dia - mond ring turns · brass, ·
3. If that · bil - ly goat gets · bon - y,

Pa-pa's goin' to buy you a mock-ing bird. · If that mock-ing
Pa-pa's goin' to buy you a look-ing glass. · If that look-ing
Pa-pa's goin' to buy you a Shet-land po - ny. If that po - ny

bird don't sing, Pa-pa's goin' to buy you a dia - mond ring.
glass gets broke, Pa-pa's goin' to buy you a bil - ly goat.
runs a - way, Pa-pa's goin' to buy you an - oth - er some day.

Winkum, Winkum

Traditional

1. Wink-um, Wink-um, shut your eye, Sweet, my ba-by, lull - a - by,
2. Chick-ens long have gone to rest, Birds lie snug with-in their nest,

For the dews are fall - ing soft, Lights are flick-'ring up a - loft;
And my bird-ie soon will be Sleep-ing like a chick-a - dee;

64

And the moon-light's peep-ing o - ver Yon-der hill-top white with clo-ver.
For with on - ly half a try, · Wink-um, Wink-um shuts her eye. ·

The Little Sandman

Johannes Brahms

1. The flow-rets all are sleep-ing Be - neath the moon's bright ray,
2. The birds that sang so sweet - ly When noon-day sun rose high,
3. Now see, the lit - tle sand-man At the win-dow shows his head,

They nod their heads to - geth - er And dream the night a - way.
With - in their nests are sleep-ing, Now night is draw-ing nigh.
And looks for all good chil - dren, Who ought to be in bed;

The bud-ding trees wave to and fro, And mur-mur soft and low.
The crick-et as it moves a-long A - lone gives forth its song.
And as each wea-ry pet he spies Throws sand in-to its eyes.

1,2,3. Sleep · on, sleep · on, Sleep on, my lit - tle one!

Listen to "The Little Sandman (Instrumental)," Brahms. (Victor Listening Album One)

We put more coal on the big red fire,
And while we are waiting for dinner to cook,
Our father comes and tells us about
A story that he has read in a book.

And when we are sitting very still,
He sings us a song or tells a piece,
He sings, "Dan Tucker Went to Town,
Or tells us about the golden fleece.

Elizabeth Madox Roberts

Winter Lullaby

Mary Webster

K. G. W. Taubert

mi (3)

1. Sleep, my ba - by, sleep, · Wrapped in slum - ber deep; ·
2. Sleep, my ba - by, sleep, · Wrapped in slum - ber deep; ·

Dark is all the win - ter night, Slow - ly fall the snow-flakes light;
Snow-flakes love the frost - y night, Ba - by loves his cra - dle white;

la la la la si la ti mi

Robed in fleec - y white they wan - der, From the si - lent spac - es yon - der,
He is lulled by moth-er's sing-ing, They on leaf-less boughs are swing-ing,

Ba - by now must go to rest, Safe on moth - er's breast. ·
Drow - sy winds are croon - ing low, Off to sleep they go. ·

66

Moon's Lullaby

Marian Mitchell

Churchill-Grindell

do (1)   so (5)

1. All through the night when wee bird-ies are sleep-ing,
2. Why must the moth-er moon sing un-til morn-ing?

In the sky old moth-er moon Sings in sweet tones to her
Don't the star ba-bies a - wake? Yes, but how man-y she

twin-kling star ba-bies A sooth-ing and beau-ti-ful croon.
sings in-to slum-ber, No won-der it takes her till day.

CHORUS

Lull - a - by, lull - a - by, lit - tle star ba - bies,

In - to your cloud beds creep. Fuzz - y bird ba - bies now

dream in your cra - dles, Lull - a - by, lull - a - by, sleep.

Sweet and Low

Alfred Tennyson

Joseph Barnby

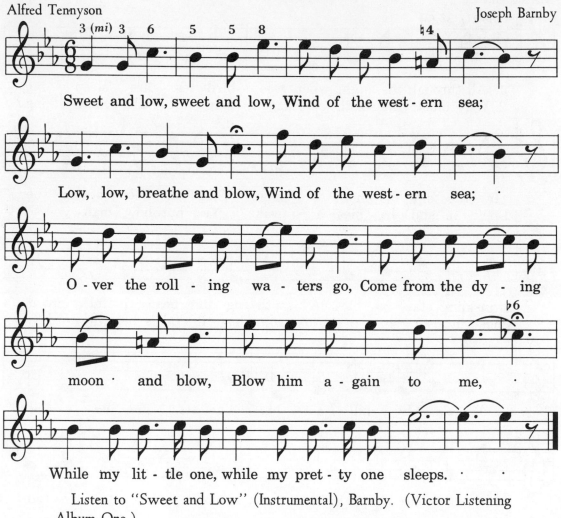

Sweet and low, sweet and low, Wind of the west - ern sea;

Low, low, breathe and blow, Wind of the west - ern sea;

O - ver the roll - ing wa - ters go, Come from the dy - ing

moon and blow, Blow him a - gain to me,

While my lit - tle one, while my pret - ty one sleeps.

Listen to "Sweet and Low" (Instrumental), Barnby. (Victor Listening Album One.)

Hush-A-Bye, Birdie

Scottish Lullaby

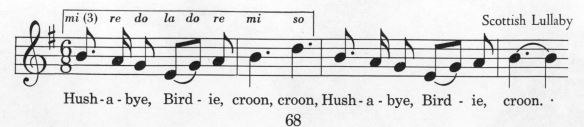

Hush - a - bye, Bird - ie, croon, croon, Hush - a - bye, Bird - ie, croon.

The sheep are gone to the sil - ver wood

And the cows · are gone to the broom, broom.

Broom is a kind of shrub which grows in Scottish pastures.

Go to Sleep

Translated

Finnish Folk Song

mi
dm   dm   dm   gm   A7

Go to sleep, my lit - tle Au - no[1], now it's time for slum - ber.

la   si   la
dm   gm   dm   A7   dm

See the twin-kling stars are wink-ing, what an end - less num - ber.

dm   dm   gm   dm   A7

Soon the moon will rise and shine on us from o'er the hill - top.

dm   gm   dm   gm   A7   dm

Go to sleep, my lit - tle Au - no, now it's time for slum - ber.

[1] Pronounce Au like *ou* in *out*

69

Little Carl Must Go to Rest

Translated by H. Jacobson

Old Swedish Lullaby

la mi mi re mi do ti   *do mi mi do ti la*

1. Lit - tle Carl must go to rest, Go to sleep, my ba - by;
2. Lull - a - by, now rest your head, Sleep, my dar - ling ba - by;
3. Moth - er rocks her ba - by dear, Lull - a - by, my ba - by;

Lit - tle birds are in their nest, Go to sleep, my ba - by;
You shall have your horse and sled, Sleep, my dar - ling ba - by;
Heav'n - ly an - gels guard thee here, Lull - a - by, my ba - by;

All the world in slum - ber lies, Soon to wake with sun - ny skies,
You shall have your ti - ny house, If you're qui - et as a mouse,
Ti - ny shoes and coat of gold Keep my dar - ling from the cold,

Go to sleep, my ba - by.
Sleep, my dar - ling ba - by.
Lull - a - by, my ba - by.

Cradle Song

Kwakiutl Indian

so (5) mi la

Sleep-o, sleep-o, lit-tle owl - et,   Sleep-o, sleep-o, lit-tle bear,

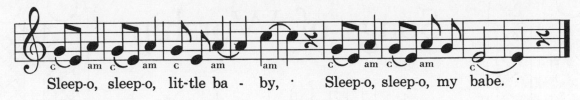

Sleep-o, sleep-o, lit-tle ba - by, · Sleep-o, sleep-o, my babe. ·

Listen to "Pueblo Lullaby-Wium." (Victor Indian Album for Elementary Grades.)

Lullaby

American Negro

O Moth-er Glas-co, where's your lamb? I left him down in the mead-ow.

Birds and the bees sing-ing in the trees, Poor lit-tle lamb say "Mam-my."

Good Night

Translated from the German by
Christine Turner Curtis

Richard Mertens

1. The day of light and laugh - ter Is fad-ing from the skies; ·
2. And pray to God, my dear · ones, That an-gels in their flight ·

The gold - en stars are shin - ing, So close your sleep-y eyes.
Will guard you while you're sleep-ing, Good night, good night, good night.

Listen for mood to "Berceuse," Järnefelt. (Victor Listening Album Two.)

71

Songs of Worship

Prelude

Arranged from a Chorale by
Louis Bourgeois, 1551

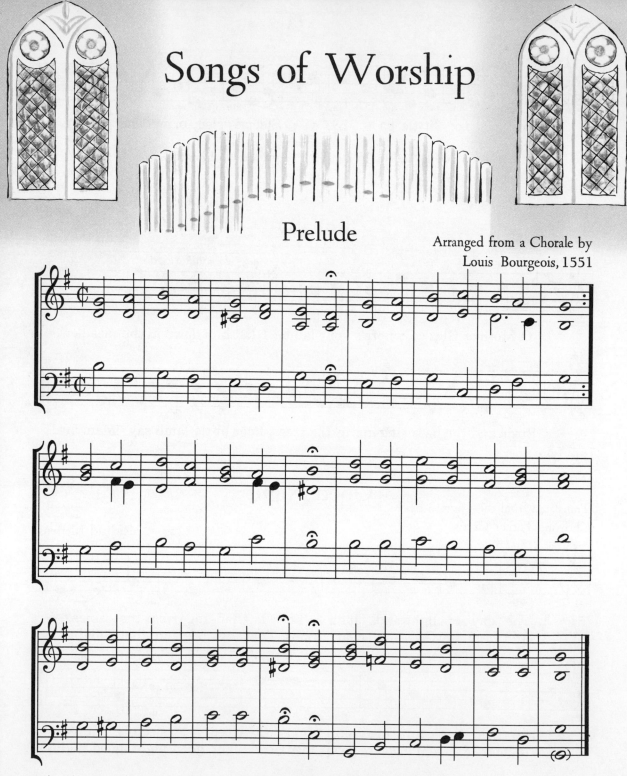

Some of you can play this on the piano.

Hear Our Prayer, O Lord

George Whelpton

3 (mi)

Hear our pray'r, O Lord, Hear our pray'r, O Lord,

In - cline Thine ear to us, And grant us Thy peace.

Praise God, from Whom All Blessings Flow

Thomas Ken, 1709

Louis Bourgeois
Genevan Psalter, 1551

do (1)

Praise God, from Whom all bless - ings flow; Praise

Him, all crea - tures here be - low; Praise Him a - bove, ye

heav'n - ly host; Praise Fa ther, Son, and Ho - ly Ghost.

Rise Up, O Men of God!

William Pierson Merrill

Arranged from Robert Schumann

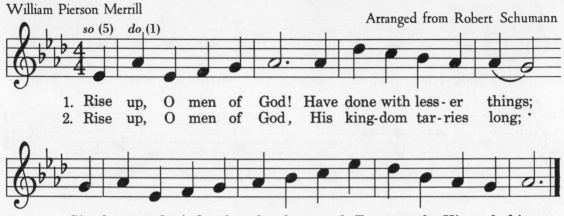

1. Rise up, O men of God! Have done with less-er things;
2. Rise up, O men of God, His king-dom tar-ries long;

Give heart and mind and soul and strength To serve the King of kings.
Bring in the day of broth-er-hood, And end the night of wrong.

Come, Thou Almighty King

George Whitfield's Hymn Book, 1757

Felice de Giardini

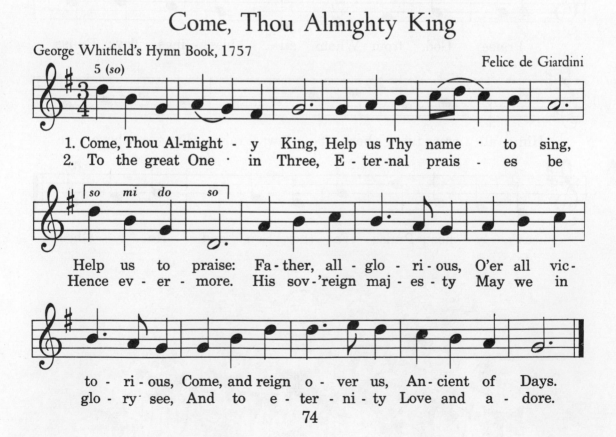

1. Come, Thou Al-might-y King, Help us Thy name to sing,
2. To the great One in Three, E-ter-nal prais-es be

Help us to praise: Fa-ther, all glo-ri-ous, O'er all vic-
Hence ev-er-more. His sov-'reign maj-es-ty May we in

to-ri-ous, Come, and reign o-ver us, An-cient of Days.
glo-ry see, And to e-ter-ni-ty Love and a-dore.

74

For Health and Strength

For health and strength and dai - ly food, We praise Thy name, O Lord.

Children of the Heavenly King

John Cennick

Ignaz J. Pleyel

Chil-dren of the heav'n-ly King, As ye jour - ney, sweet-ly sing;

Sing your Sav-iour's worth-y praise, Glo-rious in His works and ways.

Lovely Appear

Charles François Gounod

Love - ly ap - pear o - ver the moun - tains The

feet of them that preach, and bring good news of peace, The

feet of them that preach, and bring good news of peace.

Songland People

Billy Boy

Traditional

mi (3)

1. Oh, · where have you been, Bil - ly Boy, Bil - ly Boy, Oh, ·
2. Did she bid you to come in, Bil - ly Boy, Bil - ly Boy, Did she
3. Can she make a cher-ry pie, Bil - ly Boy, Bil - ly Boy, Can she
4. How · old · is · she, Bil - ly Boy, Bil - ly Boy, How ·

where · have you been, charm-ing Bil - ly?   I have
bid you to come in, charm-ing Bil - ly?   Yes, she
make a cher - ry pie, charm-ing Bil - ly?   She can
old · is · she, charm-ing Bil - ly?   Three times

do   la

been to seek a wife, She's the joy · of my life, She's a
bade me to come in, There's a dim - ple in her chin, She's a
make a cher - ry pie, Quick's a cat can wink her eye, She's a
six and four times sev'n, Twen-ty-eight · and e - lev'n, She's a

so   mi   so   so   fa   re   ti   re   do

1, 2, 3, 4. young thing and can - not leave her moth - er. ·

76

Oh! Susanna

Stephen Collins Foster

1. I came from Al - a - bam-a, With my ban - jo on my knee, I'm
2. I had a dream the oth- er night When ev-'ry-thing was still; I

goin' to Lou - si - a - na, There my true love for to see; It
thought I saw Su - san -na dear, A - com-ing down the hill; A

rained all night the day I left, The weath- er it was dry, The
buck-wheat cake was in her mouth, A tear was in her eye; Says

sun so hot I froze to death, Su - san-na, don't you cry.
I, "I'm com- ing from the South, Su - san-na, don't you cry."

CHORUS

fa fa la la la so so mi do re

Oh! Su - san - na, Oh, don't you cry for me, I've

come from Al - a - bam - a With my ban - jo on my knee.

77

The Arkansas Traveler

Adapted by Christine Turner Curtis

American Dance Tune

do (1) mi re do la la la so so do

1. Far and far a-way down in Ar-kan-sas There lived a squat-ter
2. When the rain came down on the cab-in floor, The squat-ter on-ly

with a stub-born jaw. His nose was ru-by red and his whis-kers gray,
fid-dled all the more. "Why don't you mend your roof?" said the trav-'ler bold.

And he would sit and fid-dle all the night and all the day.
"How can I mend my cab-in when the rain is wet and cold?"

Came a trav-'ler down the val-ley, Asked if he could find a bed,
"Squat-ter, pick a sun-ny morn-ing, When the air is dry and nice;

"Yes, try the road," the kind - ly squat - ter said. "Then
Patch up your cab - in, that is my ad - vice." The

could you point me out the way to find a tav - ern or an inn?"
squat-ter shook his hoar - y head and an-swered with a stub-born air,

"Quite a lit - tle piece, I reck - on, though I've nev - er been."
"Cab - in nev - er leaks a drop when days are bright and fair."

'Liza Jane

Traditional

3 (mi)

1. There's a gal in Bal - ti - more, Li'l 'Li - za Jane,
2. If you'll come and be my own, Li'l 'Li - za Jane,
3. We'll have chick-ens round our door, Li'l 'Li - za Jane,

She's the one that I a - dore, Li'l 'Li - za Jane.
We'll eat ham and sweet corn pone, 'Li'l 'Li - za Jane.
Brus - sels car - pet on our floor, 'Li'l 'Li - za Jane.

CHORUS

O E - li - za, li'l 'Li - za Jane, O E - li - za, li'l 'Li - za Jane.

79

Old Dan Tucker

Dan Emmett

Traditional

1. I went to town the oth-er night, I
2. Old Dan Tuck-er was a might-y man; He

heard the noise, then saw the fight, The watch-man was a -
washed his face in a fry-ing pan, He combed his hair with a

run-ning 'round Cry-ing, "Old Dan Tuck-er's come to town!"
wag-on wheel, And he died with a tooth-ache in his heel.

CHORUS

do mi mi do mi re do la do

So get out the way, Old Dan Tuck-er,

You're too late to stay for sup-per, Sup-per's o-ver,

break-fast's cook-ing, Old Dan Tuck-er stand-ing look-ing!

Dinah, Won't You Blow Your Horn

Traditional

Music Makers

Wolfgang Amadeus Mozart

Wolfgang Mozart seemed to be born into a world of happiness. Every day there was music in his home. His father played the clavier, which was the piano in Mozart's time. He also composed music, and sometimes led an orchestra. Often his friends brought their violins and flutes to the Mozart home and made happy music. The little baby took his first steps to music.

When Wolfgang was four years old his father began to teach him to play little minuets and other dances. At five, he played a minuet of his own making, and his father wrote it on music paper. When Wolfgang was six, his father took him and his sister on a journey to Munich in a coach drawn by two big horses. The family of three were happy making up songs most of the way.

On reaching the big city of Munich, Prince Joseph and his friends were delighted with the two charming children and had them play every night. When they left for home they were loaded with gifts. The favorite was a violin for Wolfgang.

After that when Father Mozart's friends came to make music the little boy, who was supposed to be asleep, listened and listened. One night he slipped downstairs with his violin and began playing with one of the violinists. Until then his father did not know how much the boy's ears had taught him about the violin.

In the autumn Father and Mother Mozart went with the two children to the great city of Vienna. It was a journey of a month's travel in a coach. Along the way they stopped to share their beautiful music with many people.

In Vienna the King and Queen asked the Mozart children to play for them at the castle. The King and Queen and their children heard with delight the duets played by Wolfgang and his sister. All were astonished by Wolfgang's playing and by the pieces he had composed. The Queen dressed the two little musicians in clothes which had been made for the royal family,—fine lace and satin and pearls. They wore these costumes for many concerts in other cities.

In one city Wolfgang became much excited when he heard a big orchestra play. He asked to sit by the flute player, but at the same time he was watching and listening to all the other instruments.

The Mozart family went to France and then to England, where they became great friends of the King and Queen. They stayed for nearly a year. In London, when Wolfgang was eight, he wrote his first symphony, keeping in mind the big orchestra he had heard.

The father thought Italy had much music that the boy should hear. In Rome at Easter time they heard beautiful but difficult church music. Wolfgang listened without a word, without a move, and then rushed home and wrote down every phrase of the music from memory, just as he had heard it.

Every day of Mozart's life was crowded with hours of music-making and music-writing. Happy tunes were always singing in his ears. Many of these tunes are ours today.

Two of Mozart's melodies for piano and one for violin and piano are here for some of you to play. On page 149 you will find one of Mozart's songs which all of you can sing.

Sonatina

Wolfgang Amadeus Mozart

Theme from Sonata IV

Wolfgang Amadeus Mozart

Listen to "Theme from Sonata in A Major," Mozart. (Victor Listening Album Four.)

A Melody

From "Sonata for Violin and Piano"
Wolfgang Amadeus Mozart

Listen to "Minuet from *Don Juan*," Mozart. (Victor Rhythm Album Five.)

Franz Joseph Haydn

Franz Joseph Haydn always loved to sing. Many nights his father, strumming on a harp, sang folk songs with the mother and the children. Little Franz Joseph would keep time with his make-believe violin, made of two smooth sticks.

When Franz Joseph was six years old his schoolmaster cousin came to their village to give a violin concert. He noticed the child playing his make-believe violin. The next day he heard the little boy sing, and persuaded the parents to let the child go to his school to learn music. Soon Joseph was singing the solos in his cousin's boy choir.

One day a man arrived from Vienna, looking for boy singers for the famous cathedral choir. Seven-year-old Joseph was chosen as the sweetest singer of all. Before many weeks he was singing solos in the great cathedral in Vienna. The Empress invited the choir to sing at her castle, the very same castle where Mozart had played when he was a boy of seven.

After ten years in this choir Franz Joseph's solos went to his little brother Michael, for Joseph was growing fast and his man's voice was coming. He thought, "This means I must work hard at learning to write music and playing my violin, for music keeps me happy."

He often played lively music for dancing, and sometimes he took his violin and serenaded beneath windows where a few coins were thrown to him.

One day he was invited to live in the home of a wealthy baron, to play music for his guests. This rich baron had only string players, so Haydn wrote quartets for two violins, a viola, and a cello. A melody from one of these quartets is on page 90 for some of you to play on the violin and piano.

From the baron's home he went to be the music master in Prince Esterhazy's palace, where he could write music for a big orchestra. Here, on many a morning before the sun came up, Haydn was working on a new symphony or a new quartet or trio.

Haydn always liked to play jokes. One day while visiting a country fair he spied some toy instruments: a drum, cymbals, trumpet, sleigh bells, a rattle, a triangle, and a pair of whistles, one sounding like a cuckoo and the other like a nightingale. With these toys in mind he composed the "Toy Symphony" for real instruments and toy instruments too, and to this day fun-loving people enjoy Haydn's "Toy Symphony."

When he went to England he wrote many symphonies, one called the "Surprise" Symphony. In a very quiet part there comes a crashing chord which surely is a surprise to anyone settled down for a nap. The melody that has the surprise chord in it is here for some of you to play on the piano. In his "Clock" Symphony the bassoon, cello, and bass viol keep the clock ticking, while other instruments sing the melody.

Haydn wrote the following hymn for the Emperor's birthday. Papa Haydn, as all his orchestra players called him, said it was his favorite hymn. You will find another of his songs, "The Heavens Are Telling," on page 116.

Listen to "Toy Symphony," Haydn (Victor Listening Album Three); "Theme from Andante of 'Clock' Symphony," Haydn (Victor Listening Album Five).

Glorious Things of Thee Are Spoken

John Newton

Franz Joseph Haydn

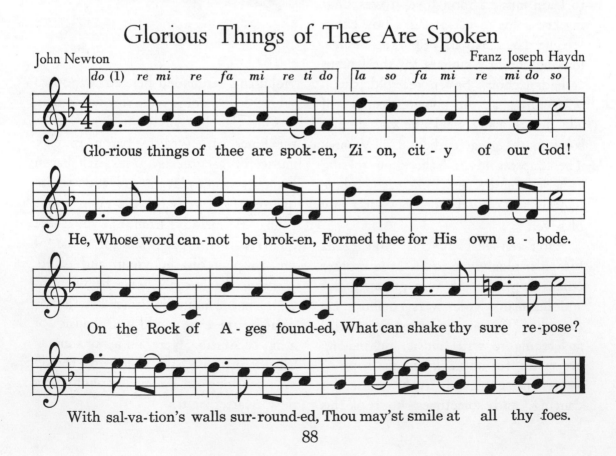

Andante

From "The Surprise Symphony"
Franz Joseph Haydn

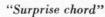

"*Surprise chord*"

Listen to "Andante from 'The Surprise Symphony'," Haydn. (Victor Listening Album Four.)

Serenade

From "String Quartet, Op 3, No. 5"
Franz Joseph Haydn

Happy Holidays

Happy Birthday

Don Pitson

Hap-py Birth-day, Hap-py Birth-day, Hap-py Birth-day to you,

Lots of pres-ents and a big cake we wish for you, too!

Hap-py Birth-day, Hap-py Birth-day, may all your dreams come true,

Hap-py Birth-day, Hap-py Birth-day, Hap-py Birth-day to you!

Birthday Greeting

M. Hauptmann

1 (do)

Ros-es we bring to you, And good wish-es sing, As your

birth-day gift and greet-ing.

91

Halloween

Heyhow for Halloween,
When all the witches are to be seen,
Some in black and some in green.
Heyhow for Halloween.

Old Scotch Rhyme

Three Little Witches

Marjorie Barrows

Paul Forde

1. Three lit-tle witch-es · pranced in the gar-den,
2. Three lit-tle witch-es · blew on their broom-sticks,

Three lit-tle witch-es · danced from the moon;
Three lit-tle witch-es · flew to their queen,

One wore a wish-ing hat, one held a puss-y-cat,
O-ver the wind-y glen in-to the night; but then,

One went a-pit-ty-pat and whis-pered a tune.
They will be back a-gain next Hal-low-een.

Listen to "Elfenspiel," Kjerulf. (Victor Rhythm Album Three.)

Hallowee-ee-een

J. G. G.

June Goethe Garrels

1. Hal - low - ee - ee - een, the witch is rid-ing high, Have you
2. There's a big black cat a - cross-ing in our way, Now you've

see - ee - een her shad - ow in the sky? So be-
heard of that — "Bad luck," they al - ways say. Weren't you

ware, don't you dare to e - ven boast or a ghost To your dis-
scared when it stared with eyes a - glow! Hear that crow! · There's a

may will hear you say that you don't care, say a pray'r Or
thump · near the pump, let's hur - ry home or a gnome Will

it may come and pull your hair.
thump a lump up - on your dome.

It will make a Jack-o'-lantern or a big
Thanksgiving pie.
It's a big round yellow something; you can
guess it if you try.

Unknown

Make a song of this poem.

The Pumpkin Man

E. L. H.

Edward L. Heth

The pump-kin man on Hal-low-een is a ter-ri-ble sight to see,

He has no arms, he has no legs, and his head is as big as

three. He has a nose that gleams and glows, his

eyes · shine bright in the night. Look out, look out for the

pump-kin man! Look out! You'd bet-ter look out! (Spoken) *Boo!*

94

Thanksgiving

T is for turkey so crispy and brown,
H is for ham with its sugary crown,
A is for apple pie grandmother makes,
N is for nuts and nice little cakes,
K is for kinsfolk who come to break bread,
S is for sauce made of cranberries red,
G is for gravy, enjoyed not the least,
I is for Indians at the first feast,
V is for voices of young and old,
I is for ice cream so dainty and cold,
N is for nonsense which makes the day bright,
G is for games we all play until night.

Amy McDonall

Thanksgiving Song[1]

Alice C. D. Riley

Jessie L. Gaynor

1. Swing the shin-ing sick-le, Cut the rip-ened grain,
2. Loud-ly blows the north wind Through the shiv-'ring trees,

Flash it in the sun-light, Swing it once a-gain.
Bare are all the branch-es, Fall-en all the leaves,

Tie the gold-en grain-heads In-to shin-ing sheaves,
Gath-ered is the har-vest For an-oth-er year,

Beau-ti-ful their col-ors As the au-tumn leaves.
Now our day of glad-ness, Thanks-giv-ing Day, is here.

[1]Reprinted by permission, from *Songs of the Child World*, No. 1, by Riley and Gaynor, published by John Church Company, copyright 1897; renewal, 1925.

Thanksgiving Day

Annette Wynne

John Langland

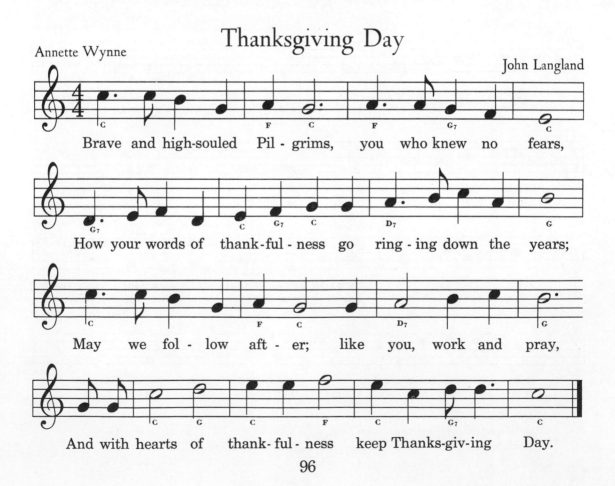

Brave and high-souled Pil - grims, you who knew no fears,

How your words of thank-ful - ness go ring - ing down the years;

May we fol - low aft - er; like you, work and pray,

And with hearts of thank- ful - ness keep Thanks-giv-ing Day.

Come, Ye Thankful People, Come

Henry Alford

George J. Elvey

1. Come, ye thank-ful peo-ple, come, Raise the song of har-vest home;
2. All the world is God's own field, Fruit un-to His praise to yield;

All is safe-ly gath-ered in, Ere the win-ter storms be-gin;
Wheat and tares there-in are sown, Un-to joy or sor-row grown;

God, our Mak-er, doth pro-vide For our wants to be sup-plied;
Rip-'ning with a won-drous pow'r Till the fin-al har-vest hour;

Come to God's own tem-ple, come, Raise the song of har-vest home.
Grant, O Lord of life, that we Ho-ly grain and pure may be.

Song of the Spirit-Dance • (Ghost-Dance Songs)

Pine Ridge, South Dakota

Hey, hey, · joy - ous feast we · now,

Hey, hey, · joy - ous feast we · now;

Eat-ing pem - mi - can, eat-ing pem - mi - can.

Praise Song

Author unknown

Old Tune

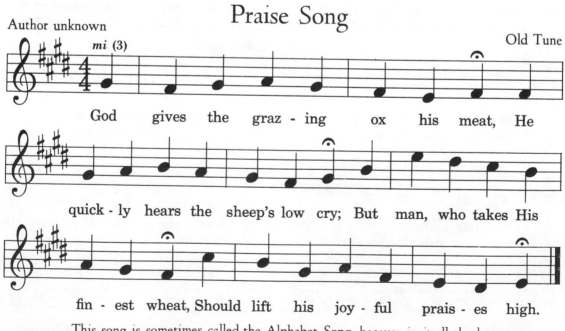

God gives the graz - ing ox his meat, He

quick - ly hears the sheep's low cry; But man, who takes His

fin - est wheat, Should lift his joy - ful prais - es high.

This song is sometimes called the Alphabet Song, because in it all the letters of the alphabet are used.

Christmas

Then be you glad, good people,
At this time of the year;
And light you up your candles,
For Christmas time is here.

Unknown

We Wish You a Merry Christmas

Cornish Folk Tune

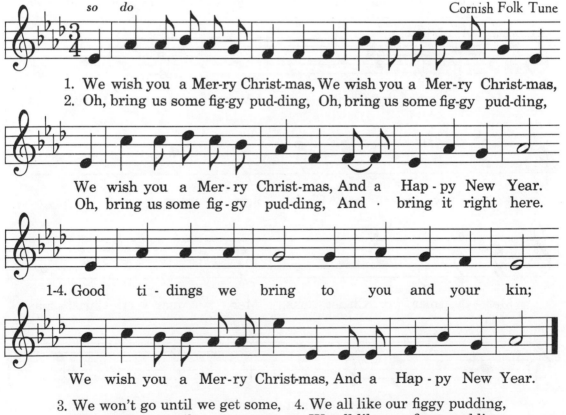

1. We wish you a Mer-ry Christ-mas, We wish you a Mer-ry Christ-mas,
2. Oh, bring us some fig-gy pud-ding, Oh, bring us some fig-gy pud-ding,

We wish you a Mer-ry Christ-mas, And a Hap-py New Year.
Oh, bring us some fig-gy pud-ding, And · bring it right here.

1-4. Good ti-dings we bring to you and your kin;

We wish you a Mer-ry Christ-mas, And a Hap-py New Year.

3. We won't go until we get some,
   We won't go until we get some,
   We won't go until we get some,
   So bring it right here.

4. We all like our figgy pudding,
   We all like our figgy pudding,
   We all like our figgy pudding,
   With all its good cheer.

Merry Christmas[1]

Alice C. D. Riley

Jessie L. Gaynor

1. Mer-ry Christ-mas now is here, Hap-piest day of all the year;
2. San-ta Claus once more has come, Has for broth-er brought a drum,

Ev-'ry face with smiles is bright, Ev-'ry heart with joy is light.
And a doll for sis-ter Sue, What did San-ta bring to you?

Mer - ry, mer - ry Christ - mas, Mer - ry, mer - ry Christ - mas,

Mer - ry, mer - ry Christ - mas, glad and gay,

Mer - ry, mer - ry Christ - mas, Mer - ry, mer - ry Christ - mas,

Mer - ry, mer - ry Christ - mas, hap - py day.

[1]From *Songs of the Child World* by Riley and Gaynor, as published and copyrighted (1897, renewal 1925) by The John Church Company. Reprinted by permission.

O Come, All Ye Faithful (Adeste Fideles)

F. Oakeley

Old Latin

do

1. O come, all ye faith - ful, Joy - ful and tri - um - phant,
2. Sing, choirs of An - gels, Sing in ex - ul - ta - tion,

O come ye, O come · ye to Beth - le - hem;
Sing, all ye cit - i - zens of heav'n · a - bove;

Come and be - hold Him, Born the King of An - gels;
Glo - ry to God · In the high - est, glo - ry!

O come, let us a - dore Him, O come, let us a - dore Him,
O come, let us a - dore Him, O come, let us a - dore Him,

O come, let us a - dore Him, · Christ, · the Lord.
O come, let us a - dore Him, · Christ, · the Lord.

101

Deck the Hall

Old Welsh Air

5 (so)

1. Deck the hall with boughs of hol-ly, Fa la la la la la la la la.
2. See the blaz-ing Yule be-fore us, Fa la la la la la la la la.
3. Fast a-way the old year pass-es, Fa la la la la la la la la.

'Tis the sea-son to be jol-ly, Fa la la la la la la la la.
Strike the harp and join the cho-rus, Fa la la la la la la la la.
Hail the new, ye lads and lass-es, Fa la la la la la la la la.

Don we now our gay ap-par-el, Fa · la la la la la la.
Fol-low me in mer-ry meas-ure, Fa · la la la la la la.
Sing we joy-ous all to-geth-er, Fa · la la la la la la.

Troll the an-cient Yule-tide car-ol, Fa la la la la la la la la.
While I tell of Yule-tide treas-ure, Fa la la la la la la la la.
Heed-less of the wind and weath-er, Fa la la la la la la la la.

It Came Upon the Midnight Clear

Edwin H. Sears

Richard S. Willis

so mi

It came up-on the mid-night clear, That glo-rious song of old,

From an-gels bend-ing near the earth, To touch their harps of gold:

102

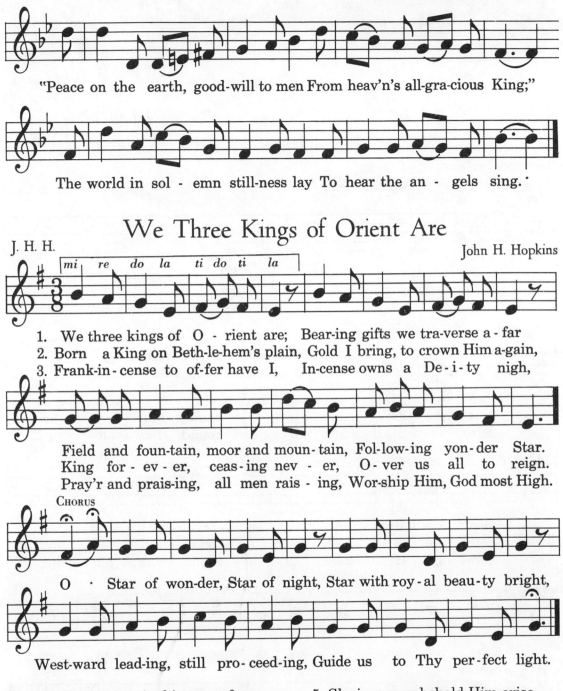

"Peace on the earth, good-will to men From heav'n's all-gra-cious King;"

The world in sol - emn still-ness lay To hear the an - gels sing.

We Three Kings of Orient Are

J. H. H.

John H. Hopkins

mi re   do   la   ti do ti   la

1. We three kings of O - rient are; Bear-ing gifts we tra-verse a - far
2. Born   a King on Beth-le-hem's plain, Gold I bring, to crown Him a-gain,
3. Frank-in - cense to of-fer have I,   In-cense owns a De-i-ty   nigh,

Field and foun-tain, moor and moun-tain, Fol-low-ing yon-der Star.
King for - ev - er, ceas-ing nev - er, O - ver us all to reign.
Pray'r and prais-ing,   all men rais - ing, Wor-ship Him, God most High.

CHORUS

O · Star of won-der, Star of night, Star with roy - al beau-ty bright,

West-ward lead-ing, still pro - ceed-ing, Guide us to Thy per-fect light.

4. Myrrh is mine, its bitter perfume
   Breathes a life of gathering gloom,
   Sorrowing, sighing, bleeding, dying,
   Sealed in the stone-cold tomb.

5. Glorious now behold Him arise,
   King and God and sacrifice,
   Alleluia, Alleluia,
   Earth to the heav'ns replies.

103

Here Lies a Baby

Translated by Johanna C. F. Auer
Paraphrased by Janet Tobitt

Netherlands Carol

1. Here lies a Ba - by, O come and be - hold,
2. Young shep - herds, haste, to the sta - ble draw nigh,
3. Come, lit - tle an - gels, ap - proach to your King,

See how He's cry - ing and shiv - 'ring with cold,
Soothe the sweet Lamb with a soft lull - a - by,
Sure - ly He'll smile if a - round Him you sing,

See how He's cry - ing and shiv - 'ring with cold.
Soothe the sweet Lamb with a soft lull - a - by.
Sure - ly He'll smile if a - round Him you sing.

CHORUS

Na, na, na, na, na, na, sleep, my Ba - by, sleep,

Hush, hush, my Ba - by dear, please do not weep.

104

The Friendly Beasts

Twelfth Century Carol

do (1)

1. Je - sus our broth - er, kind and good, Was hum - bly born in a sta - ble rude; The friend - ly beasts a - round Him stood, Je - sus our broth - er, kind and good.

2. "I," said the donkey, shaggy and brown,
   "I carried His mother up hill and down;
   I carried His mother to Bethlehem town.
   I," said the donkey shaggy and brown.

3. "I," said the cow all white and red,
   "I gave Him my manger for His bed,
   I gave Him my hay to pillow His head.
   I," said the cow all white and red.

4. "I," said the sheep with curly horn,
   "I gave Him my wool for His blanket warm,
   He wore my coat on Christmas morn.
   I," said the sheep with curly horn.

5. "I," said the dove from the rafters high,
   "I cooed Him to sleep that He should not cry,
   We cooed Him to sleep, my mate and I.
   I," said the dove from rafters high.

6. Thus every beast, by some good spell,
   In the stable dark was glad to tell
   Of the gift that he gave Emmanuel.
   The gift that he gave Emmanuel.

This Is the Time of Joy

Susanna Myers

French Carol

do (1)

1. Though bit-ter cold the win-try night, It is the hour most ho - ly,
2. Come with your gifts and join the crowd, For-get-ting wind and weath-er,

When we must go to see the Child Who lies in man-ger low - ly.
Out on the road to Beth-le-hem, We glad-ly go to-geth-er.

Chorus

mi fa so do re ti do

This is the time of joy, And all must do Him hon - or,

No lov-ing heart will fail To bring Him gifts and hon - or.

O Jesu Sweet

English version by Christine Turner Curtis

S. Scheidt, 1650

1. O Je - su[1] sweet, O Je - su mild, Thou
2. O Je - su sweet, O Je - su mild, Thy

art the Fa - ther's ho - ly Child, From heav'n come
Moth - er looked on Thee and smiled, Then sent Thee

[1]Pronounce yā′sōō

down to do His will, His lov - ing pur - pose to ful -
forth with man to share, This life of sor - row and of

fill. O Je - su sweet, O Je - su mild.
care. O Je - su sweet, O Je - su mild.

He Is Born, the Holy Child

Translated by Susanna Myers

French Carol

so do

He is born, the Ho - ly Child, Or - gan, flute, sweet mu - sic play!

Fine

He is born, the Ho - ly Child, Praise Him, all, this Christ-mas Day.

1. Look! He lies in a man-ger bed, He, the King of heav'n-ly glo - ry,
2. In the sky bright an-gels sing, Bring-ing us the Christ-mas sto-ry,
3. With the shep-herds and the kings, Let us kneel in love and won-der,

D.C. al Fine

Fair and soft is the Ba - by head, Cra-dled there in the man-ger bed;
Dis-tant ech-oes · joy-ful ring; Peace, good will, the an-gels sing;
Ask-ing hum-bly · for His bless-ing, For all chil-dren · as they sing;

I Heard the Bells

Henry W. Longfellow

John B. Calkin

1 (do) 3 #2 3 3 4 3 4 ♮4 5 8 7 6 6 5 5

1. I heard the bells on Christ-mas day Their old, fa-mil-iar car-ols play,
2. I thought how, as the day had come, The bel-fries of all Chris-ten-dom

And wild and sweet the words re-peat Of peace on earth, good will to men.
Had rolled a-long the un-brok-en song Of peace on earth, good will to men.

New Year Song

Northwest School Children
Marlborough, Connecticut

1 (do)

F   F   C₇   F

1. The New Year's in, the Old Year's out, The peo-ple gath-er round and shout.
2. The whis-tles blow, the bells do ring, The peo-ple dance and shout and sing.

B♭   F   C₇   F

1, 2. "Hap-py New Year, one and all!" Is what the joy-ous peo-ple call.

One of you play this on the piano while the others sing.

Patriotic Days

Hats off!
Along the street there comes
A blare of bugles, a ruffle of drums,
A flash of color beneath the sky.
Hats off!
The flag is passing by!

Henry Holcomb Bennett

Flag Song

Lydia Avery Coonley Ward

Walter Evans

1. Out on the breeze, O'er land and seas, A beau-ti-ful ban-ner is
2. O-ver the brave Long may it wave, Peace to the world ev-er

stream-ing, Shin-ing its stars, · Splen-did its bars, ·
bring-ing, While to the stars · Linked with the bars ·

Un-der the sun-shine 'tis gleam-ing. Hail to the flag, The
Hearts will for-ev-er be sing-ing: Hail to the flag, The

dear, bon-ny flag—The flag that is red, white, and blue. ·
dear, bon-ny flag—The flag that is red, white, and blue. ·

1, 2. Hail to the flag, The dear, bon-ny flag—The flag that is red, white, and blue.

Listen to "Stars and Stripes Forever," Sousa. (Columbia or Victor record.)

A heart that was brave and strong and sure,
A soul that was noble and great and pure,
A faith in God that was held secure—
This was George Washington.

America

Samuel Francis Smith
Traditional

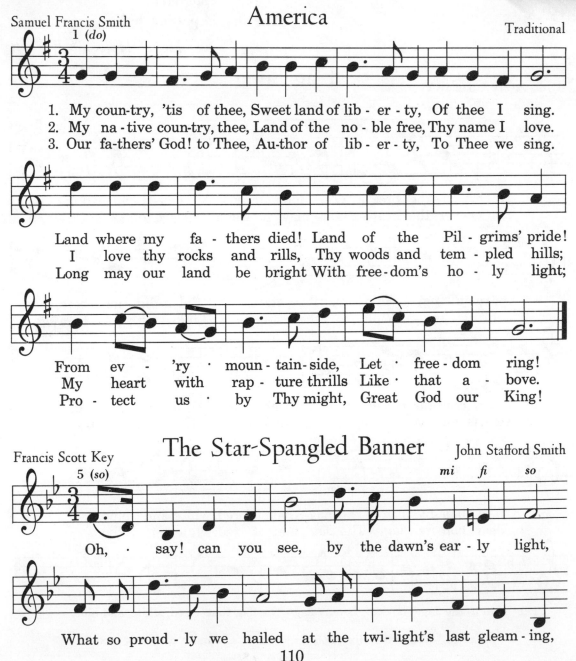

1 (do)

1. My coun-try, 'tis of thee, Sweet land of lib - er - ty, Of thee I sing.
2. My na - tive coun-try, thee, Land of the no - ble free, Thy name I love.
3. Our fa-thers' God! to Thee, Au-thor of lib - er - ty, To Thee we sing.

Land where my fa - thers died! Land of the Pil - grims' pride!
I love thy rocks and rills, Thy woods and tem - pled hills;
Long may our land be bright With free-dom's ho - ly light;

From ev - 'ry · moun - tain-side, Let · free - dom ring!
My heart with rap - ture thrills Like · that a - bove.
Pro - tect us · by Thy might, Great God our King!

The Star-Spangled Banner

Francis Scott Key
John Stafford Smith

5 (so)

mi   fi   so

Oh, · say! can you see, by the dawn's ear - ly light,

What so proud - ly we hailed at the twi - light's last gleam - ing,

110

Whose broad stripes and bright stars, through the per - i - lous fight,

O'er the ram - parts we watched were so gal - lant - ly stream-ing?

And the rock - ets' red glare, the bombs burst-ing in air,

Gave proof through the night that our flag was still there.

Oh, say does that Star-span-gled Ban - ner yet wave ·

O'er the land · of the free and the home of the brave?

. . . I see him, as he stands
With gifts of mercy in his outstretched hands.

From "Lincoln,"
by George Henry Boker

Battle Hymn of the Republic

Julia Ward Howe

William Steffe

5 (so)

Mine eyes have seen the glo - ry of the com - ing of the Lord;

He is tram-pling out the vin-tage where the grapes of wrath are stored;

He hath loosed the fate - ful light - ning of His

ter - ri - ble swift sword; His truth is march - ing on.

CHORUS

Glo - ry, glo - ry, Hal - le - lu - jah! Glo - ry, glo - ry, Hal - le - lu - jah!

Glo - ry, glo - ry, Hal - le - lu - jah! His truth is march-ing on.

112

Valentine's Day

I Have a Little Valentine

Mary C. Parsons

Charles J. Cromwell

I have a lit - tle val - en-tine That some-one sent to me. It's

pink and white and red and blue, As pret - ty as can be. For -

get - me -nots are round the edge, And ti - ny ros - es too; And

such a love - ly piece of lace — The ver - y pal - est blue. And

in the cen - ter there's a heart, As red as red can be! And

ritard

on it's writ - ten all in gold, "To You, with Love from me."

If apples were pears,
And peaches were plums,
And roses had a different name;
If tigers were bears,
And fingers were thumbs,
I'd love you just the same.

Unknown

One, He Loves

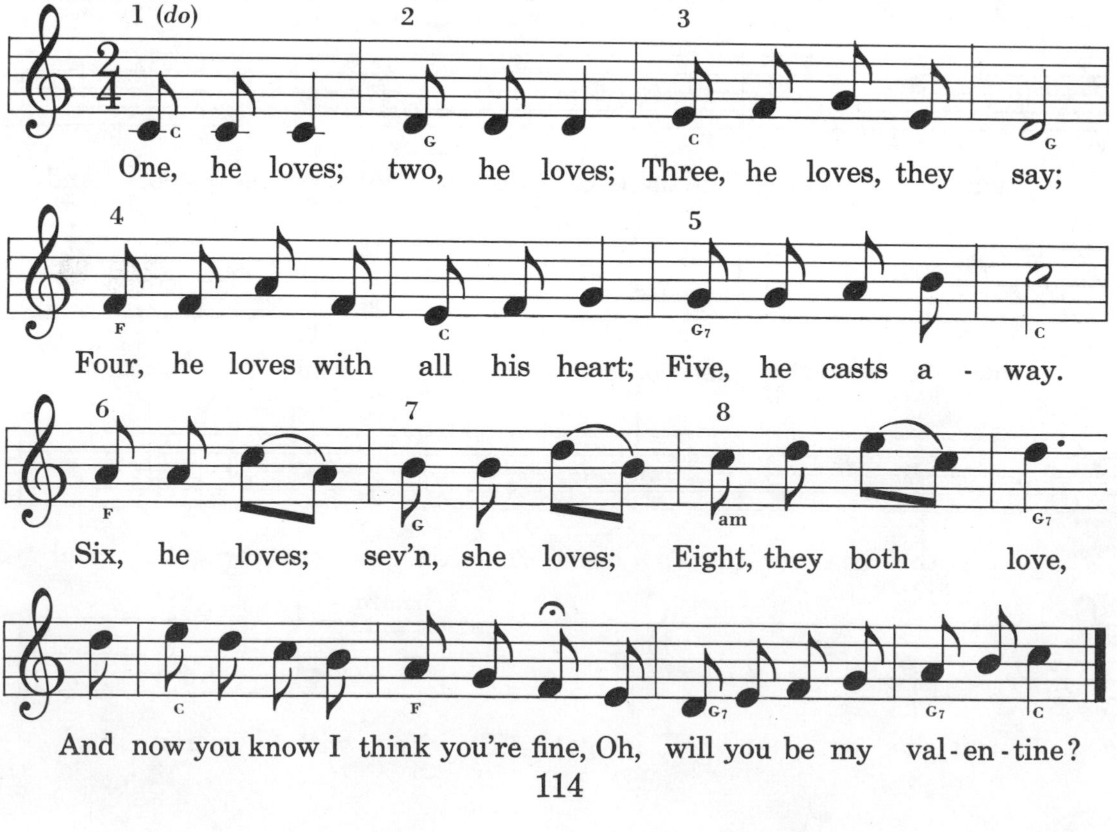

1 *(do)*   **2**   **3**

One, he loves; two, he loves; Three, he loves, they say;

4   **5**

Four, he loves with all his heart; Five, he casts a - way.

6   **7**   **8**

Six, he loves; sev'n, she loves; Eight, they both love,

And now you know I think you're fine, Oh, will you be my val-en-tine?

114

Valentine

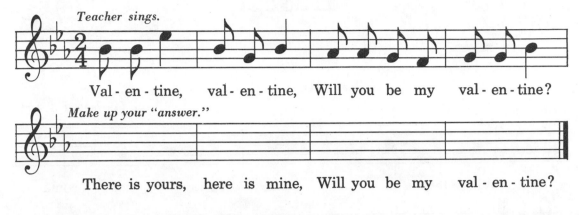

Teacher sings.

Val - en - tine,   val - en - tine,   Will you be my   val - en - tine?

Make up your "answer."

There is yours,   here is mine,   Will you be my   val - en - tine?

Easter

Winter Is O'er

Giovanni Palestrina

so

Win - ter is o'er and spring has come,

The vic - to - ry of life is won;

The song of tri - umph has be - gun. Al - le - lu - ia!

The Heavens Are Telling · From "The Creation"

Psalm 19

Franz Joseph Haydn

5 (so) 8 (do)

The hea - vens are tell - ing the glo - ry of God,

The won - der of His work dis - plays the fir - ma - ment.

The won - der of His work dis - plays the fir - ma - ment.

116

THE WONDERFUL WORLD OUTSIDE

You friendly Earth! how far do you go,
With the wheat fields that nod and the
rivers that flow,
With cities and gardens, and cliffs and isles,
And people upon you for thousands of miles?

William B. Rands

Earth and Sky

The Wonderful World

William Brighty Rands

Henry M. Halvorson

do (8)

Great,   wide,   beau - ti - ful, won - der - ful   World, ·

re   ti   so

With the   won - der - ful   wa - ter round you   curled, ·   ·

And the   won - der - ful   grass up - on   your   breast —   ·

ritard

World, ·   ·   you   are   beau - ti - f'ly   dressed!   ·

When I Climb a Hill

Aileen Fisher

Ronald Avery

When I climb a hill that is high, high, high,

There's noth-ing a-head but the hill and sky;

When I reach the top and can see, see, see,

ti ti do ti la so fa mi re do

There's a world of things in front of me.

Mists of Daybreak

Buson (Japanese)

With gentle motion

The mists of day-break seem · To paint as with a

fair-y brush A land-scape in a dream. ·

You can play this song on the black keys of the piano.

119

Morning Song

18th Century English

The sun is ris - ing out of bed, And in the east the sky is red; Then up and wake each sleep - y head, So ear - ly in the morn - ing. 'Tis shame to dream the hours a - way, When all the world is bright with day, And na - ture calls to work and play So ear - ly in the morn - ing.

Lovely Evening

Three-part Round

Oh, how love - ly is the eve - ning, is the eve - ning,

When the bells are sweet - ly ring - ing, sweet - ly ring - ing,

Ding, dong, ding, dong, ding, dong.

Lovely Evening (Parts for clarinet)

Three-part Round

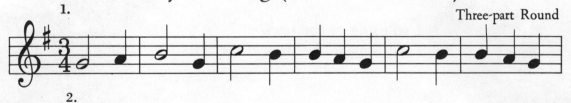

Out of the Earth Come Good Things

Robin Christopher

8 (do)

James Seton

1. Out of the earth come good things, And out of the sky, the sun; · And out of the clock the min - utes Come one, by one, by one. ·

2. Out of the day the night comes, And out of the dark - 'ning blue, · The twin - ka - ling red and gold stars Come two, by two, by two. ·

I will sing to the trees,
I will sing to the stars in the skies.

Sara Teasdale

Stars

Kansas City School Children

so   do

I   like   to   see   the   stars   in   the   deep blue sky   at   night

And   I   like   to   see   the   sun   ap-pear with bright and glow-ing light,

But I know that when the day is done the sun-ny light will go

And I will see the stars a-gain from here on earth be-low.

Clouds

Unknown

Adapted from "The Chimes of Normandy"

White · sheep, white · sheep, On a blue hill, on a blue hill,

When the wind stops, when the wind stops, You all stand still.

When the wind blows, when the wind blows, You walk a - way slow.

White · sheep, white · sheep, Where do you go? Where do you go?

You can play this song on melody instruments.

The Lovely Moon

Eleanor Farjeon[1]

Henry M. Halvorson

The moon, the love-ly moon, When the town's a-sleep, ·

fa so fa re mi so fi so la ti so

In her sil-ver beau-ty Wan-ders down the steep, ·

Wan-ders down the steep · Un-seen by you and me ·

In all her sil-ver beau-ty To walk up-on the sea. ·

Listen to "Clair de Lune," Debussy. (Victor Listening Album Five.)

Night Song

Words from Pennsylvania Military College

U. S. Bugle Call "Taps"

Fad-ing light dims the sight, And a star gems the sky, gleam-ing

bright. From a-far draw-ing nigh, Falls the night.

From *A Collection of Poems* by Eleanor Farjeon. Used by permission of the Author
and W. Collins Sons & Co., Ltd., Publishers.

124

Rain, Wind and Water

The Rain

W. E.

Walter Evans

do (8)   *la*   *do*

How beau-ti-ful is the rain · As the shin-ing rain-drops fall; ·

so mi

They sound like ti-ny drum-mers · On top my par-a-sol. ·

When I go in for shel-ter, · Look out the win-dow pane, ·
The leaves are set a-quiv-'ring, · The flow-ers nod a-gain, ·

I watch the ti-ny riv-ers.   How beau-ti-ful is the rain.
The gar-den shines like sil-ver.   How beau-ti-ful is the rain.

Laughed the brook for my delight
Through the day and through the night.

John Greenleaf Whittier

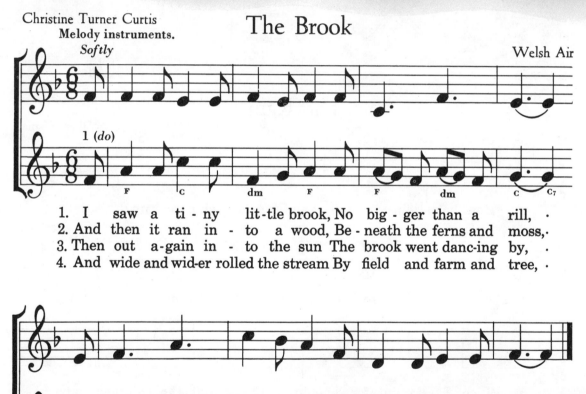

Christine Turner Curtis
Melody instruments.

The Brook

Welsh Air

Softly

1 (*do*)

F　C　dm　F　F　dm　C　C₇

1. I saw a ti-ny lit-tle brook, No big-ger than a rill, ·
2. And then it ran in-to a wood, Be-neath the ferns and moss,·
3. Then out a-gain in-to the sun The brook went danc-ing by, ·
4. And wide and wid-er rolled the stream By field and farm and tree,·

F　F　C₇　F　gm　C₇　F

Come leap-ing from the moun-tain-side And rip-ple down the hill. ·
No big-ger than a sil-ver thread That I could jump a-cross.·
Its wa-ters flow-ing fast and deep Be-neath the sum-mer sky. ·
Un-til a state-ly riv-er ran To meet the shin-ing sea. ·

The River Song

Bryant School Children

so (5)

I like the riv-er song, It seems to roll a-long,

Then we see the bright yel-low moon. This is our riv-er song.

Make up a song of your own about a river.

Rivers of China

Luther Wilde

Chinese Folk Tune

mi mi so la do la so so la so

1. Wa - ters of Chi - na, in pond and in pool,
2. Riv - ers of Chi - na that nour - ish the grains,

Shad - ed with grass - es so green and so cool,
Bear - ing the junks from the hills to the plains,

Ringed with the lo - tus, lil - y of gold,
Down through the rice - fields, un - der the sky,

You mir - ror pa - go - das and tem - ples old.
Your wide flow - ing wa - ters go roll - ing by.

Listen to "The Moldau," Smetana. (Columbia or Victor record.)

Down the Stream

Derrick Norman Lehmer Collection

Miwok Indian Song

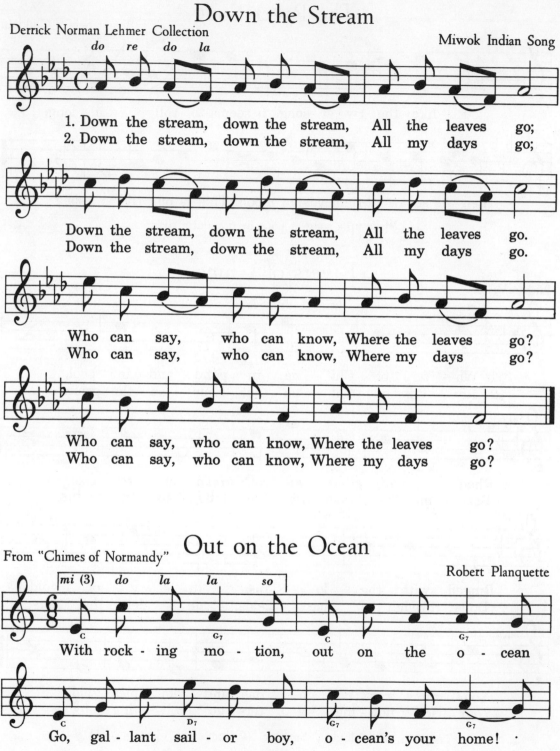

do re do la

1. Down the stream, down the stream, All the leaves go;
2. Down the stream, down the stream, All my days go;

Down the stream, down the stream, All the leaves go.
Down the stream, down the stream, All my days go.

Who can say, who can know, Where the leaves go?
Who can say, who can know, Where my days go?

Who can say, who can know, Where the leaves go?
Who can say, who can know, Where my days go?

Out on the Ocean

From "Chimes of Normandy"

Robert Planquette

mi (3) do la la so

With rock - ing mo - tion, out on the o - cean

Go, gal - lant sail - or boy, o - cean's your home!

128

Calm you'll be sleep - ing while gales are sweep - ing.

O'er the great o - cean of wa - ters you roam.

Boating on the Lake

Theodor Kullak, Op. 62

Some of you can play this on the piano.

Listen to "Boating on the Lake," Kullak. (Victor Rhythm Album Two.)

It made a rustling sound
As softly through the leaves it blew,
But now it roughly swirls around
And seems to say: "Boo-oo."

Unknown

Make a song of this poem.

The North Wind

Unknown

Paul Forde

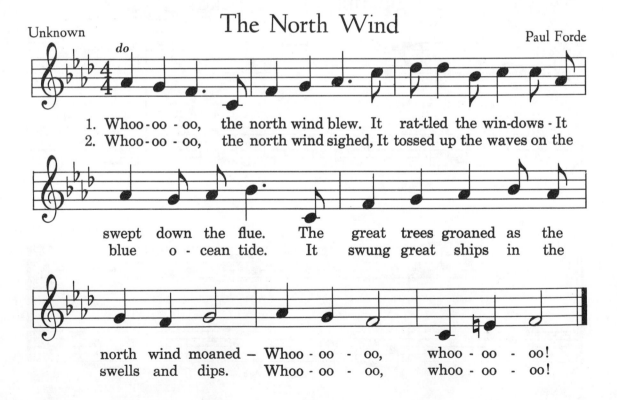

do

1. Whoo-oo-oo, the north wind blew. It rat-tled the win-dows - It
2. Whoo-oo-oo, the north wind sighed, It tossed up the waves on the

swept down the flue. The great trees groaned as the
blue o-cean tide. It swung great ships in the

north wind moaned - Whoo-oo-oo, whoo-oo-oo!
swells and dips. Whoo-oo-oo, whoo-oo-oo!

Listen to "The Wind on the Plain" (Prelude No. 3), Debussy. (Columbia or
Victor record.)

Ships

Nancy Byrd Turner

Ethel Anthony

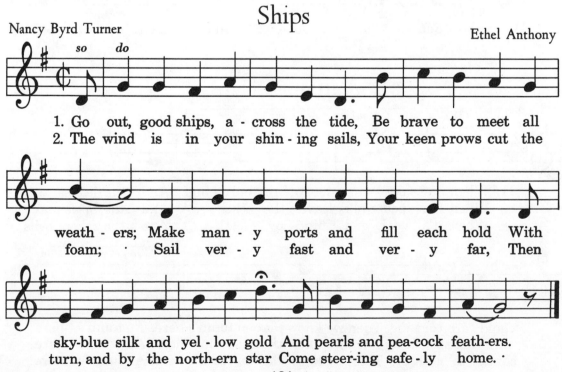

so do

1. Go out, good ships, a - cross the tide, Be brave to meet all
2. The wind is in your shin - ing sails, Your keen prows cut the

weath - ers; Make man - y ports and fill each hold With
foam; Sail ver - y fast and ver - y far, Then

sky-blue silk and yel - low gold And pearls and pea-cock feath-ers.
turn, and by the north-ern star Come steer-ing safe - ly home.

131

Autumn

September brings us heaps of corn,
With harvest days all bright and warm.

Thirty Days Has September

Old Tune

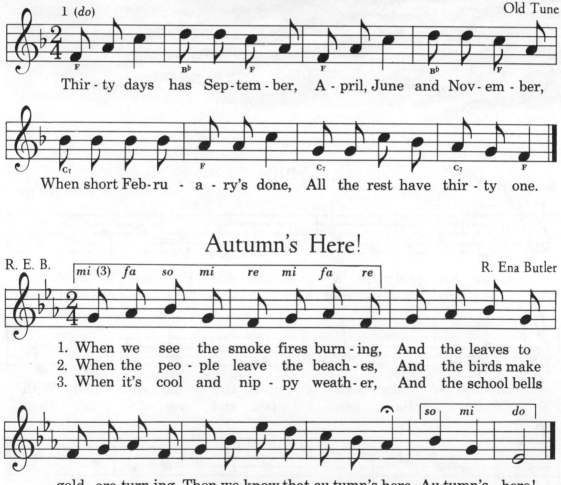

Thir - ty days has Sep - tem - ber, A - pril, June and Nov - em - ber,

When short Feb - ru - a - ry's done, All the rest have thir - ty one.

Autumn's Here!

R. E. B.

R. Ena Butler

1. When we see the smoke fires burn - ing, And the leaves to
2. When the peo - ple leave the beach - es, And the birds make
3. When it's cool and nip - py weath - er, And the school bells

gold are turn - ing, Then we know that au - tumn's here, Au - tumn's here!
fare - well speech - es, Then we know that au - tumn's here, Au - tumn's here!
chime to - geth - er, Then we know that au - tumn's here, Au - tumn's here!

Red Leaves, Gold Leaves

Teacher sings.

Red leaves, gold leaves fall from the trees;

You make your "answer."

Hear them rus - tling in the breeze.

Fun in the Leaves

Christine Turner Curtis

Lydia Elwood

so

1. When leaves are heaped be-side the walk up - on my way to town,
2. Or some-times I will tun - nel there, and then I will pre - tend

I like to make a fly - ing leap, and then come div - ing down
That I'm a rab - bit or a mole with - out a sin - gle friend,

In - to the moun - tain of the leaves, so dry and brown.
And I must dig my bur - row deep at sum-mer's end.

Raking Leaves

Christine Turner Curtis

Henrietta Evans

You rake the ma-ple leaves, I'll rake the oak, Red leaves and
yel-low leaves make pur-ple smoke. You rake the lin-den leaves,
I'll rake the ash, Brown leaves and gold-en leaves Burn in a flash.
You rake the pop-lar leaves, I'll rake the birch;
See how the sparks fly up, High as the church.

Rake leaves to "Waltz No. 1," Brahms. (Victor Rhythm Album Two.)

The Harvest Home

Translated by Cecil Cowdrey

French Folk Song

1. Gai-ly my bag-pipes sound, Our sons with hon-or greet-ing,
2. On now with dance and song, The tunes of old re-peat-ing.

134

Clear-eyed and true of heart, From har-vest toil they come.
On this be-lov-èd soil We'll tread *The Har - vest Home.*

Sung at Harvest Time

English version by Christine Turner Curtis

Inca Melody

mi mi la so

1. Come, my sis-ters, come, my broth-ers, At the sound-ing of the horn;
2. Praise to thee, O might-y In - ti,[1] For the bar-ley and the cane!

do   do la so la do

On the hill-sides, on the moun-tains, Har-vest we the yel-low corn.
In the wheat fields, in the corn fields, Har-vest we the yel-low grain.

Gold-en shines our Fa-ther Sun;   Sil-ver shines our Moth-er Moon;
Soft-ly blows the au-tumn wind;   Gen-tly wave the silk-en leaves;

Sick-les flash-ing, fill your bas-kets, Reap-ing in the yel-low noon.
Reap-ers sing-ing, press we on-ward, Ty - ing up the yel-low sheaves.

[1] Pronounced In-*tē* and means "sun god."

Jack Frost

Helen Bayley Davis · Charles Leonhard

mi (3) mi ri ri mi mi do do so la do mi so

Some-one paint-ed pic-tures on my win-dow pane last night,

Wil-low trees with trail-ing boughs and flow-ers, frost-y white,

And love-ly crys-tal but-ter-flies. But when the morn-ing sun

Touched them with its gold-en beams, They van-ished one by one!

Winter

Winter brings us ice,
Skates and sleds and sleighing nice.

Winter Has Come

Translated

German Folk Song

1. A,   a,   a,   Oh, win-ter came to-day!
2. E,   e,   e,   On ice and snow we ski.
3. I,   i,   i,   Do not the poor pass by.

Fall and sum-mer now have part-ed, Win-ter frol-ics now have start-ed,
Flow-ers bloom in hous-es on-ly, For out-doors the air is frost-y,
Give them clothes to keep them warm, or Frost and cold will do them harm. ·

A,   a,   a,   Yes, win-ter came to-day!
E,   e,   e,   On ice and snow we ski.
I,   i,   i,   Do not the poor pass by.

4. O, o, o, How happily we go
To the stall where in a manger
Lies the Blessèd Little Stranger.
O, o, o, How happily we go.

5. U, u, u, We know what we shall do.
Love the Christ-child, help the lowly,
Feed the hungry, cheer the lonely.
U, u, u, We know what we shall do.

The Merry Skaters

Mary Vaughan

German Folk Tune

so   so mi do

1. The ice is spar - kling cold and clear, The
2. We skim the ice in cir - cles wide, As

laugh - ing girls and boys are here, And skates so mer - ri - ly
round and round we swift - ly glide, And gai - ly, cheer - i - ly

ring, ring, And skates so mer - ri - ly ring; As
sing, sing, And gai - ly, cheer - i - ly sing; As

1, 2. o'er the ice we go, Heigh - o! Heigh - o! Heigh - o! As

o'er the ice we go, Heigh - o! Heigh - o! Heigh - o!

Skating

Teacher sings.

Skat - ing, skat - ing, skat-ing, heigh - ho!

You make up your "answer."

O-ver the ice a - way we go.

We Can Go Out Coasting

Mary Baker

Marian Murdock

do

1. Crys-tal flow'rs are fall-ing from a dark-ened sky;
2. Gen - tly fall - ing blos-soms give the trees a crown;

We can go out coast - ing, you and I.
White and sil - ver snow-flakes make earth's gown.

Frost - y feath-ers, star - like, flut - ter soft-ly by;
Frost - y feath-ers, star - like, flut - ter soft-ly by;

We can go out coast - ing, you and I.
We can go out coast - ing, you and I.

139

Jingle Bells

J. Pierpont

1. Dash-ing through the snow   In a   one-horse o-pen sleigh,
2. Now the ground is white,   Go   it while you're young,

O'er the fields we go,   Laugh-ing all   the   way;
Take the girls to-night,   And   sing this sleigh-ing   song;   Just

Bells on bob-tail ring,   Mak-ing spir-its bright;   What
get a   bob-tailed nag,   Two-for-ty   for his speed,   Then

fun it is   to ride and sing A sleigh-ing song to-night!
hitch him to   an   o-pen sleigh, And crack! you'll take the   lead.

Chorus

Jin-gle bells! Jin-gle bells! Jin-gle   all   the way!

Oh, what fun   it   is   to ride in a   one-horse o-pen sleigh!

140

Jin - gle bells! Jin - gle bells! Jin - gle all the way!

Oh, what fun it is to ride in a one-horse o - pen sleigh.

Listen to "The Sleigh Ride from 'German Dances'," Mozart. (Victor record.)

Mister Snowman

C. J. C.

Polish Folk Tune

Mis - ter Snow - man, here's a hat for you, sir;
coat
pipe

It's an old hat, but it's good as new, sir;
coat,
pipe,

You may wear it if you hur - ry, do, sir;
wear
smoke

You'll be melt - ing in a day or two, sir.

141

The Snow Is Dancing

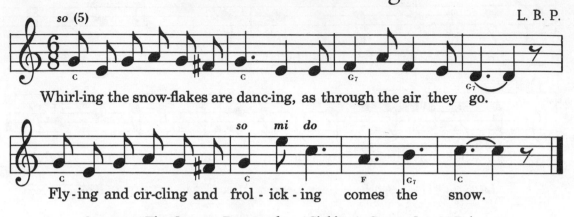

L. B. P.

Whirl-ing the snow-flakes are danc-ing, as through the air they go.

Fly-ing and cir-cling and frol-ick-ing comes the snow.

Listen to "The Snow is Dancing from 'Children's Corner Suite'," Debussy. (Columbia or Victor record.)

Gently the Snow Is Falling

Translated

French

Gen-tly the snow is fall - ing, Float-ing a-round and round, ·

Trem-bling like but-ter - flies, But-ter-flies fly - ing by. ·

Cov - er-ing hills and gar - dens, Branch-es and bend-ing leaves, ·

Gen-tly the snow is fall - ing, Down from the clouds on high. ·

Spring

Spring is coming! Spring is coming!
How do you think I know?
I found some pussy-willows,
So I know it must be so.

Unknown

All the Birds Will Soon Be Here

Translated

German Folk Song

1. All the birds will soon be here, Win-ter winds are fly - ing.
2. Mer - ry birds are on the wing, North-ward they are fly - ing.

Love-ly mu-sic soon will sound, Chirp-ing, pip-ing, all a - round,
Rob-in, star-ling, thrush and swal-low, Scold-ing blue-jay, sing-ing spar-row,

Twit - ter-ing and coo - ing too. Spring will soon be com - ing.
Bob - o - link and blue - bird too. Spring will soon be com - ing.

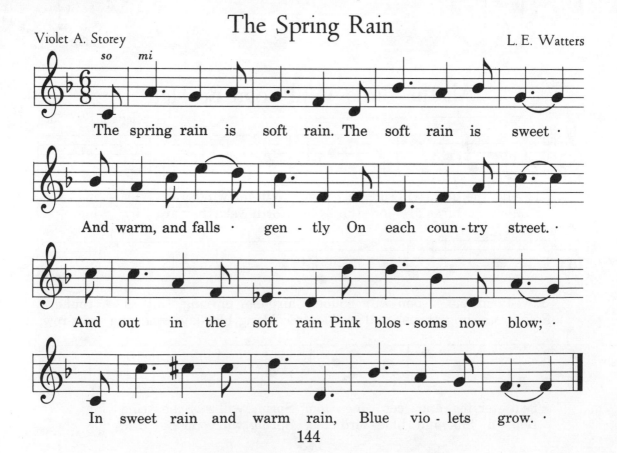

. . . rich in flowers and trees,
Humming birds and honey bees.

John Greenleaf Whittier

The Spring Rain

Violet A. Storey

L. E. Watters

so *mi*

The spring rain is soft rain. The soft rain is sweet ·

And warm, and falls · gen - tly On each coun - try street. ·

And out in the soft rain Pink blos - soms now blow; ·

In sweet rain and warm rain, Blue vio - lets grow. ·

144

Away to the Meadows

Old Song

Come to the mead-ows where prim-ros-es grow,

But-ter-cups look-ing as yel-low as gold, Dai-sies and cow-slips be-

gin-ning to bloom, 'Tis a most beau-ti-ful sight to be-hold.

Bus-y bees hum-ming a-bout them are seen,

But-ter-fly hap-pi-ly flut-ters a-long; Grass-hop-pers chirp in the

hedg-es so green, Lin-net is sing-ing his live-li-est song.

Listen to "The Swiss Maid (Spring Dance)," Traditional. (Victor Rhythm
Album Five.)

Little Man in the Woods (Jack-in-the-pulpit)

Translated

From *Hansel and Gretel*, Humperdinck

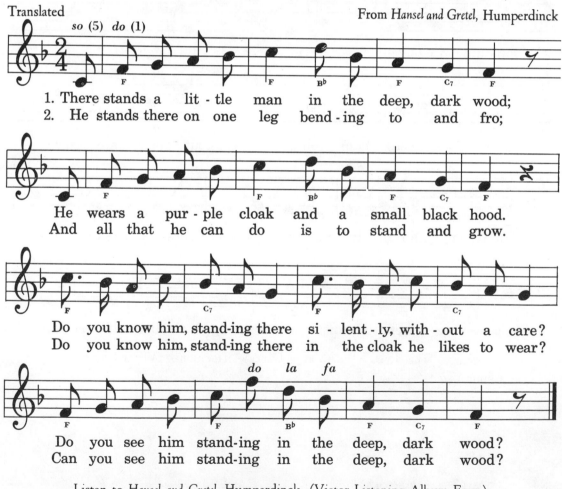

so (5) *do* (1)

1. There stands a lit-tle man in the deep, dark wood;
2. He stands there on one leg bend-ing to and fro;

He wears a pur-ple cloak and a small black hood.
And all that he can do is to stand and grow.

Do you know him, stand-ing there si-lent-ly, with-out a care?
Do you know him, stand-ing there in the cloak he likes to wear?

do la fa

Do you see him stand-ing in the deep, dark wood?
Can you see him stand-ing in the deep, dark wood?

Listen to *Hansel and Gretel*, Humperdinck. (Victor Listening Album Four.)

Rowing to Camp

C. J. C. Charles J. Cromwell

1. Row - ing, row - ing, Dip - ping the oars and pull - ing strong.
2. Row - ing, row - ing, Back to the camp at riv - er's side.

Spring sun shin - ing, Warm as we float a - long.
Spring sun set - ting, Home in the e - ven - tide.

Spring Garden

C. J. C. Charles J. Cromwell

1. Now we are plant - ing a gar - den. That is a
2. Flow - ers will grow in the gar - den. Breez - es will

sign it is spring, you know. Show - ers will wa - ter the
car - ry a sweet per - fume. There will be dai - sies and

gar - den, Sun - shine will make it grow.
pop - pies, Lark - spur and pinks in bloom.

Play "Spring Garden" as a duet on melody instruments.

Maypole Dance

Christine Turner Curtis

Ruth McConn Spencer

1. On a morn-ing in spring when the yel-low-birds sing
2. On a morn-ing in spring when the yel-low-birds sing

We will dance in a ring a-round the May-pole.
We will dance in a ring a-round the May-pole.

To the fields we will go, where but-ter-cups grow;
Rib-bons twine, red and blue, a curt-sey or two,

We will skip in a row a-round the May-pole.
Then we'll waltz in the dew a-round the May-pole.

Sweet in the ear-ly morn-ing, song fills the mead-ow,
Blues, make an in-ner cir-cle, Reds, twirl a-bout you,

D. C. al Fine

Each take a col-ored stream-er then wind as we go.
Turn, glide, and then a hop-step and curt-sey a-new.

Listen to "Country Dance," Weber. (Victor Rhythm Album Four.)

The Sunrise Tints the Dew

Unknown (Japanese)

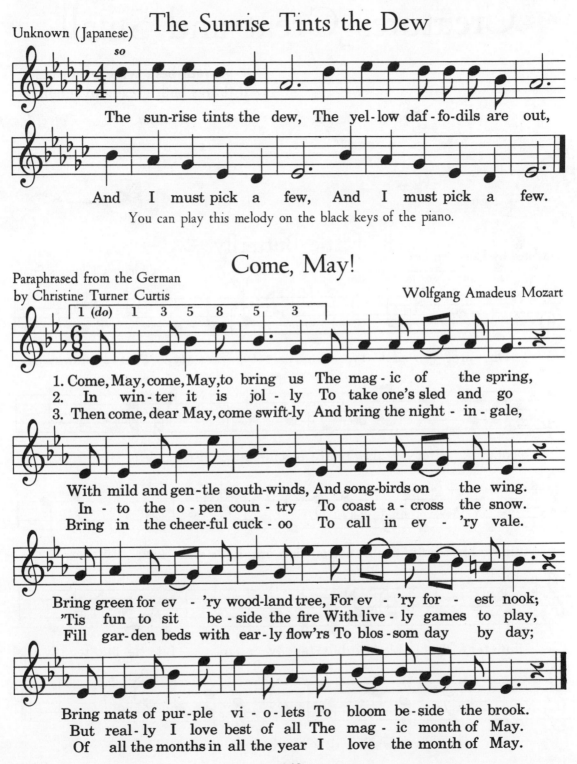

so

The sun-rise tints the dew, The yel-low daf-fo-dils are out,

And I must pick a few, And I must pick a few.

You can play this melody on the black keys of the piano.

Come, May!

Paraphrased from the German
by Christine Turner Curtis

Wolfgang Amadeus Mozart

1 (*do*) 1 3 5 8 5 3

1. Come, May, come, May, to bring us The mag-ic of the spring,
2. In win-ter it is jol-ly To take one's sled and go
3. Then come, dear May, come swift-ly And bring the night-in-gale,

With mild and gen-tle south-winds, And song-birds on the wing.
In-to the o-pen coun-try To coast a-cross the snow.
Bring in the cheer-ful cuck-oo To call in ev-'ry vale.

Bring green for ev-'ry wood-land tree, For ev-'ry for-est nook;
'Tis fun to sit be-side the fire With live-ly games to play,
Fill gar-den beds with ear-ly flow'rs To blos-som day by day;

Bring mats of pur-ple vi-o-lets To bloom be-side the brook.
But real-ly I love best of all The mag-ic month of May.
Of all the months in all the year I love the month of May.

149

Creatures Great and Small

He prayeth best, who loveth best
All things both great and small.

Samuel Taylor Coleridge

Little Butterfly

Translated by Pao-ch'en Lee

Chinese Children's Song

so mi re do do

Oh, pret-ty, pret-ty, Oh, pret-ty, pret-ty, Pret-ty flow'rs are bloom-ing, Pret-ty flow'rs are bloom-ing; Lit-tle but-ter-fly - o, Lit-tle but-ter-fly - o, Dance on flow-ers high and low; Flut-ter, fly, flut-ter, fly, Lit-tle but-ter-fly - o, Lit-tle but-ter-fly - o. How I wish I were a lit-tle but-ter-fly.

The Bee's a Busy Peddler

Nancy Byrd Turner

Marian Murdock

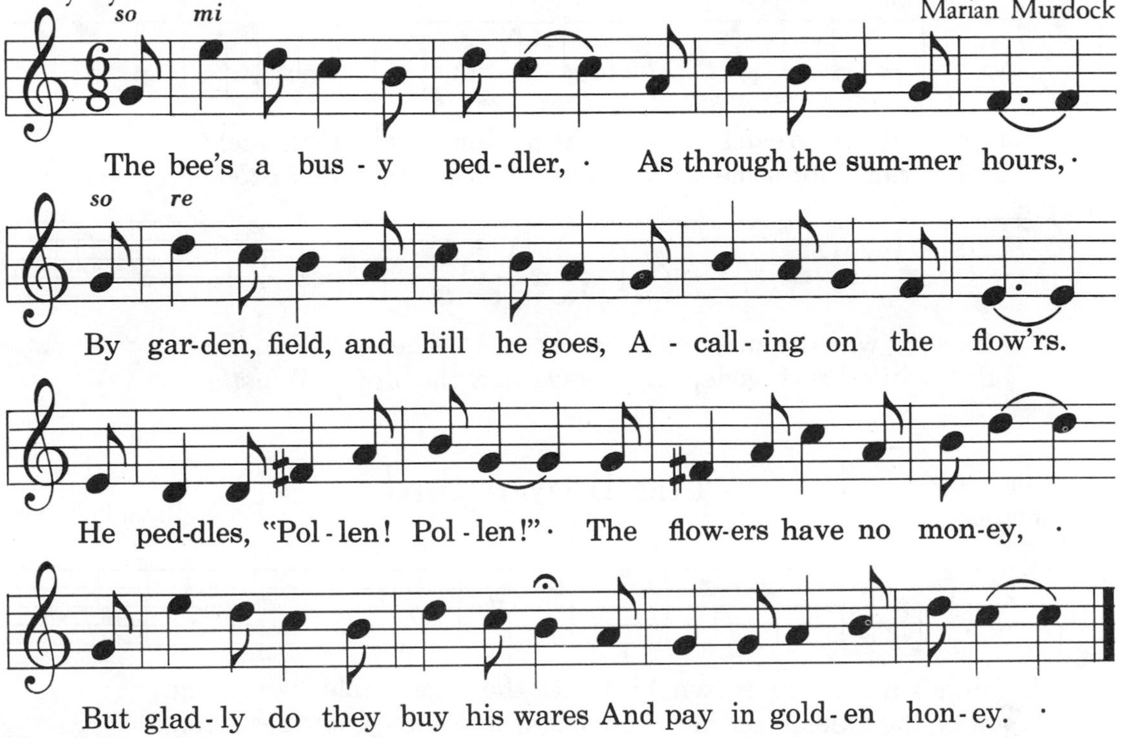

The bee's a bus-y ped-dler, · As through the sum-mer hours, ·

By gar-den, field, and hill he goes, A-call-ing on the flow'rs.

He ped-dles, "Pol-len! Pol-len!" · The flow-ers have no mon-ey, ·

But glad-ly do they buy his wares And pay in gold-en hon-ey. ·

There was an owl lived in an oak,
Wisky, wasky, weedle;
And every word he ever spoke
Was fiddle, faddle, feedle.

Traditional

Make a song of this poem.

A Little Green Bird

Jane Rensen

so *do*

1. A lit-tle green bird sat on a fence rail. (*Whistle*)· · · ·
2. I ran for some salt to put · on its tail. (*Whistle*)· · · ·

Its song was the sweet-est, ev-er I · heard. (*Whistle*)· · · ·
But while I was gone, a - way flew the bird. (*Whistle*)· · ·

The Brown Bird

After the original
by Christine Turner Curtis

Puerto Rican Folk Song

do mi re

1. There's a ti - ny brown bird on the ga - ble sing - ing,
2. May the skies bless her slum-ber where she is rest - ing,

so re do

Lull - a - by and sweet dreams to my dear one bring - ing.
And the ti - ny brown bird in the eaves is nest - ing.

so re *so la mi*

Sing, mer - ry song - bird, where she is sleep - ing,
Sing, drow - sy song - bird, care - less of sor - row,

so ti re do

And the an - gels a - bove her their watch are keep - ing.
May she dream on in safe - ty un - til to - mor - row.

Listen to "The Birds," Respighi. (Victor record.)

Fol-de-rol and Riddle-ma-ree

Michael Lewis

James Seton

Fol - de - rol and rid - dle - ma - ree, Come and join my ju - bi - lee.

I'm the riddle and I'm the key,

I'm the robin up in the tree,

I'm the river that runs to the sea,

I'm the flag that's flying free,

I'm the salmon that's on a spree,

I'm the faun that's taught to flee,

I'm the flower that's caught a bee,

I am all that I ought to be —

So I sing for ver - y glee Fol - de - rol and rid - dle - ma - ree.

153

The Squirrel[1]

Appalachian Mountain Folk Song
Collected and arranged
by Cecil J. Sharp

1. The squir-rel is a pret-ty lit-tle thing, It
2. The par-tridge is a pret-ty lit-tle bird, It
3. The rac-coon's tail is ringed a-round, The

car-ries a bush-y tail; It eats up all the
car-ries a speck-led breast; It steals a-way the
pos-sum's tail is bare; The rab-bit's got no

farm-er's corn And cracks it on the rail, And
farm-er's grain And car-ries it to his nest, And
tail at all, But a lit-tle bunch of hair, But a

cracks it on the rail, And cracks it on the rail.
car-ries it to his nest, And car-ries it to his nest.
lit-tle bunch of hair, But a lit-tle bunch of hair.

A Possum Hunt

Mississippi Singing Game

1. Pos-sum up a 'sim-mon tree, See them eyes,
2. Dogs are all a-bark-ing, Bow wow wow!
3. Pos-sum is a-ly-in' On the ground,
4. Pos-sum up a 'sim-mon tree, Shook him down,

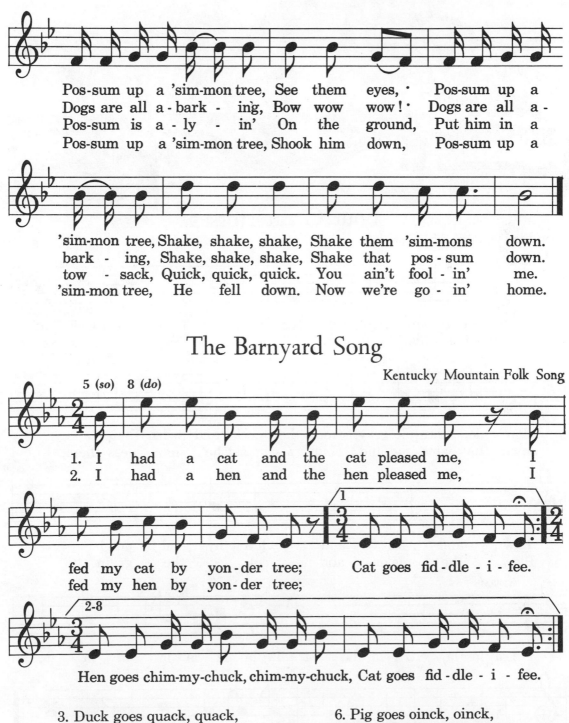

Pos-sum up a 'sim-mon tree, See them eyes, · Pos-sum up a
Dogs are all a-bark-ing, Bow wow wow! · Dogs are all a-
Pos-sum is a-ly-in' On the ground, Put him in a
Pos-sum up a 'sim-mon tree, Shook him down, Pos-sum up a

'sim-mon tree, Shake, shake, shake, Shake them 'sim-mons down.
bark-ing, Shake, shake, shake, Shake that pos-sum down.
tow-sack, Quick, quick, quick. You ain't fool-in' me.
'sim-mon tree, He fell down. Now we're go-in' home.

The Barnyard Song

Kentucky Mountain Folk Song

5 (so) 8 (do)

1. I had a cat and the cat pleased me, I
2. I had a hen and the hen pleased me, I

fed my cat by yon-der tree; Cat goes fid-dle-i-fee.
fed my hen by yon-der tree;

Hen goes chim-my-chuck, chim-my-chuck, Cat goes fid-dle-i-fee.

3. Duck goes quack, quack,
4. Goose goes sssss, sssss,
5. Sheep goes baa, baa,

6. Pig goes oinck, oinck,
7. Cow goes moo, moo,
8. Horse goes neigh, neigh,

155

Four Great Horses

Translated by Alma Alice Turechek

Czech Folk Song

1. Four great hors-es at the gate Toss their heads of
2. Wear-ing his new cap of green, Pe-pi-chek comes

dap-ple, dap-ple gray, Stretch their necks and swish their tails,
down the wind-ing lane. Four a-breast he'll har-ness them,

Paw and snort and whin-ny and neigh.
Plow the fields and cut the grain.

REFRAIN

Tra la la, tra la la, tra la la la la la la la la,

Tra la la, tra la la, tra la la la la la.

Off to the Country

Teacher sings.

1. John is off to the coun - try To help with the work to - day.
2. Sheep are out in the pas - ture, Old Dob-bin is in his stall.

Make up your "answer."

Oh, it's fun in the coun-try, I know he will like to stay.
Cows are deep in the clo-ver, Just o - ver the gar - den wall.

Evening Song

C. J. C.

Charles J. Cromwell

1. Set - ting sun is glow - ing, cat - tle are low - ing,
2. Dis - tant lights come twin - kling, sheep bells are tin - kling,

Twi - light o'er the val - ley gen - tly will fall.
Dark - er now the shad - ows; rest comes to all.

Here, Rattler, Here

Pioneer Folk Song

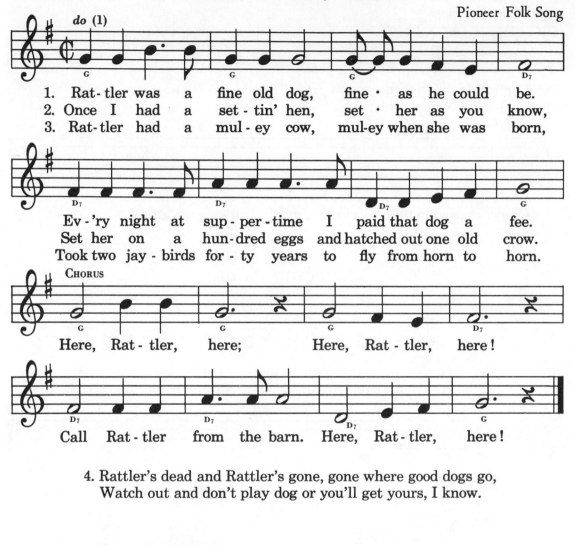

1. Rat-tler was a fine old dog, fine as he could be.
2. Once I had a set-tin' hen, set her as you know,
3. Rat-tler had a mul-ey cow, mul-ey when she was born,

Ev-'ry night at sup-per-time I paid that dog a fee.
Set her on a hun-dred eggs and hatched out one old crow.
Took two jay-birds for-ty years to fly from horn to horn.

CHORUS

Here, Rat-tler, here; Here, Rat-tler, here!

Call Rat-tler from the barn. Here, Rat-tler, here!

4. Rattler's dead and Rattler's gone, gone where good dogs go,
Watch out and don't play dog or you'll get yours, I know.

Halka Had a Rooster Red

Translated by Leonard Borowicz

Polish Folk Song

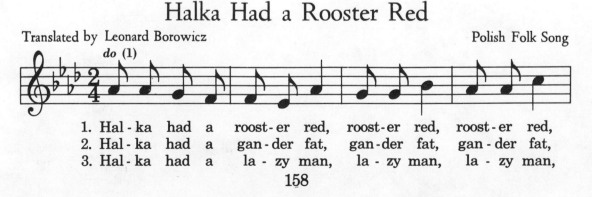

1. Hal-ka had a roost-er red, roost-er red, roost-er red,
2. Hal-ka had a gan-der fat, gan-der fat, gan-der fat,
3. Hal-ka had a la-zy man, la-zy man, la-zy man,

And she kept him in a shoe, in a shoe, hi!
And she cooked him in a pan, in a pan, hi!
And she pushed him in a trough, in a trough, hi!

so ti re fa la so mi mi

That's a good place for you, roost-er,
That's a good place for you, gan-der,
That's a good place for you, mis-ter,

In a shoe, old roost-er, in a shoe, old roost-er,
In a pan, fat gan-der, in a pan, fat gan-der,
In a trough of wa-ter, full of i-cy wa-ter,

Oh, · that's a good place for you, roost-er,
Oh, · that's a good place for you, gan-der,
Oh, · that's a good place for you, mis-ter,

In a shoe, old roost-er, in a shoe, hi!
In a pan, fat gan-der, in a pan, hi!
In a trough of wa-ter, i-cy cold, hi!

Oh, Poor Chick-a-biddy

la do fa la

Johannes Brahms

do (1)

1. Oh, poor chick-a-bid-dy, chick-a-bid-dy's gone, where has she gone?
2. Oh, poor chick-a-bid-dy, chick-a-bid-dy's gone, where has she gone?
3. Come, poor chick-a-bid-dy, chick-a-bid-dy, come, chick-a-bid-dy, do.

Where · is my chick-a-bid-dy, where has she gone?
Where · is my chick-a-bid-dy, where has she gone?
All · day, my chick-a-bid-dy, I've looked for you.

Have you seen my chick-a-bid-dy run-ning?
I must try to keep the tears from flow-ing,
Here are crumbs and gold-en grain to feed thee,

She is small, but she is quick and cun-ning.
For I need to see where I am go-ing.
They're for you if on-ly you will heed me.

Oh, poor chick-a-bid-dy, chick-a-bid-dy's gone, where has she gone?
Oh, poor chick-a-bid-dy, chick-a-bid-dy's gone, where has she gone?
Come, my chick-a-bid-dy, won't you come to me, won't you come and see?

Where is my chick-a-bid-dy, where has she gone?
Where is my chick-a-bid-dy, where has she gone?
Here is a feast of good things, wait-ing for thee.

160

Up Yonder

Translated by Margareta Wassali

Swiss Folk Song

1. Up yon-der on the moun-tain There stands a big brown
2. The hired · man starts milk - ing, But does - n't like the
3. He puts a - side his pail And he danc - es with the

Hei - de - li - domm,[1] Up yon - der on the moun - tain,
Hei - de - li - domm, The hired · man starts milk - ing,
Hei - de - li - domm, He puts a - side the pail And

CHORUS

There stands a big brown cow. Sing tra la la la, sing tra la la la!
But does - n't like the job.
he danc - es with the maid.

Tra la la la la, sing tra la la! Sing tra la la la,

sing tra la la la! Tra la la la la la la la la!

4. And while the two are dancing,
The cow steps in the Heidelidomm,
And while the two are dancing,
The cow steps in the milk.

5. You lazy, lazy milkman,
Now we have curdled Heidelidomm,
You lazy, lazy milkman,
Now we have curdled the milk.

6. The moral of this story,
Don't try to milk and Heidelidomm,
The moral of this story,
Don't try to milk and dance.

[1]Pronounce high-day-lee-dom

Grasshopper Green

Anonymous

L. E. Watters

so so mi re do ti do re mi la

1. Grass-hop-per green is a com-i-cal chap, He
2. Grass-hop-per green has a quaint lit-tle house; It's

lives on the best of fare. · Bright lit-tle trou-sers,
un-der the hedge so gay. · Grand-moth-er Spi-der, as

jack-et and cap, These are his sum-mer wear. ·
still as a mouse, Watch-es him o-ver the way. ·

Out in the mead-ow he loves · to go,
Glad-ly he's call-ing the chil-dren, I know,

Play-ing a-way in the sun; · · It's hop-per-ty, skip-per-ty,
Out in the beau-ti-ful sun; · · It's hop-per-ty, skip-per-ty,

high and low, Sum-mer's the time · for fun. ·
high and low, Sum-mer's the time · for fun. ·

ABOUT SINGING THINGS

Of the bells, bells, bells, bells,
Bells, bells, bells—
To the rhyming and the chiming of the bells!

Edgar Allan Poe

Bells and Other Things

With happy voices singing,
We dance so gay and free,
And merry bells are ringing.
What fun for you and me!

Make a song of this poem.

Oranges and Lemons

English Folk Song

so   mi   so   mi   do

Oran - ges and lem - ons, say the bells of St. Clem - en's;
When will that be? · say the bells of Step - ney; ·

Fine

You owe me five far - thin's, say the bells of St. Mar - tin's.
I · do not know, · says the great bell of Bow. ·

re ti re ti so

When will you pay me, say the bells of Old Bai - ley;

D.C. al Fine

When I grow rich, say the bells of Shore - ditch.

The Bell Ringer

Frances Ford

French-Canadian Folk Song

do (1)

1. High in the stee - ple hangs the bell,
2. Old Fa - ther Si - mon's gray and worn,

Old Fa - ther Si - mon rings it well.
Old Fa - ther Si - mon's gown is torn.

Ding, dong, ding, ev - 'ry day, ev - 'ry hour, Ding, dong, ding sounds the
Ding, dong, ding, if he van - ished a - way, Ding, dong, ding, we could

peal from the tow'r. Clang, o - ver - head, calls to bed.
romp all the day. Clang, o - ver - head, calls to bed.

Some of you will enjoy singing this bell tune while others sing the song. How many times will you repeat these two measures?

Ding, dong, ding, dong, ding, dong, ding.

Echo

Translated

French Round

1. *f* *pp* *f* 2. *f* *pp* *f*

Ech - o, ech - o, please an - swer me. Ech - o, ech - o, do you hear me?

165

Oh yes, bring a flute,
A horn, and a fiddle,
And play tootle-toot,
And fiddle-de-fiddle-de-fiddle.

Make a song of this poem.

The Flute Lesson

Translated by Pao-Ch'en Lee

Chinese Folk Song

This is a pur - ple bam - boo · flute, I will teach you

how to toot. Flute a-gainst the lips, lips a-gainst the flute,

Out comes love - ly tune, tu - ra - lu - ra - lu.

My pre-cious one, that is ver - y nice - ly done; My pre-cious

one, that is ver - y nice - ly done. · · · · · ·

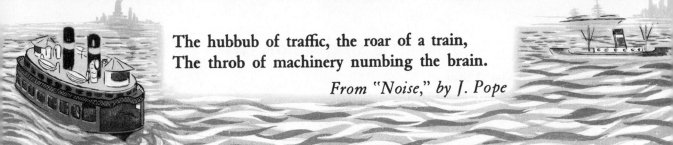

The hubbub of traffic, the roar of a train,
The throb of machinery numbing the brain.

From "Noise," by J. Pope

Sailing Across the Bay

Walter Evans

Richard C. Berg

I'd like to ride on a stream-line train And sit at the win-dow as it crossed the plain, But I'd rath-er be on a steam-boat And sail a-cross the bay; There's lots to see on the wa-ters blue, De-stroy-ers, tank-ers and cruis-ers too. I'd like to sit on the deck some day And go sail-ing a-cross the bay, And go sail-ing a-cross the bay.

Little Old Tugboat

Richard C. Berg

Oh, lit-tle old tug-boat, chug-ging right a-long, You're
not ver-y big, but you are ver-y strong. You
pull a barge and you tow a big ship, So what
mat-ter if you can-not make a ver-y fast clip.
Chug a-long, chug a-long!
Chug, chug, chug, chug! As your
Die-sels sing their song. Chug, chug,
chug, chug! As you sail on down the bay.

The Man That Runs the Crane

Richard C. Berg

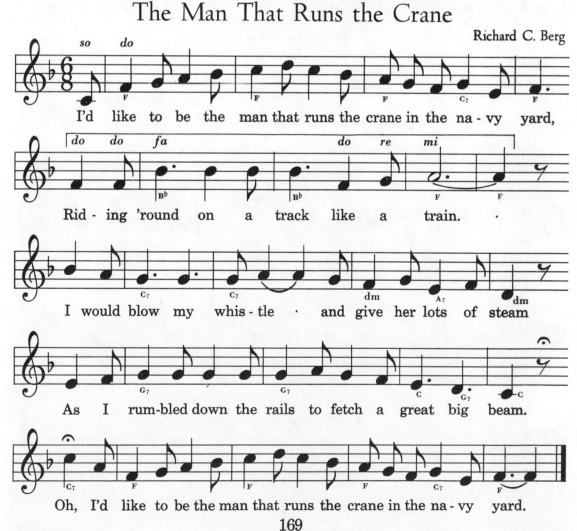

I'd like to be the man that runs the crane in the na - vy yard,

Rid - ing 'round on a track like a train.

I would blow my whis - tle · and give her lots of steam

As I rum-bled down the rails to fetch a great big beam.

Oh, I'd like to be the man that runs the crane in the na - vy yard.

We Sing and Play

We will make music wherever we go.

The Drum-Major

L. E. W.

M. White

1. See the strut-ting step to the hep, hep, hep Of the
2. Oh, the band boys play in a mar-tial way For the

proud and tall drum-ma-jor; See the white fur cap with the
proud and tall drum-ma-jor; How they keep in step to his

CHORUS

gold chin strap And the shin-ing stick he swings. Boom, boom, boom! Hear the
hep, hep, hep, And the peo-ple think he's grand. (Taa, taa, taa! Hear the

big bass drum. Boom, boom, boom! You can hear them come. The
slide trom-bones. Doo, doo, doo! Go the sax-o-phones.)

trum-pets blare a stir-ring air; Oh, hear how the march-ing mu-sic swings.

Imitate the sounds of other band instruments in the chorus.

170

Marching

Teacher sings.

Come and be my part-ner, Ma-ry, Give to me your hand;

Make up your "answer."

We will go a - march-ing To the mu-sic of the band.

It's Fun

Translated

French Folk Song

1. It's fun for all of us to know That we can sing our songs with
2. And if we like to change our fun, It works as well to start with

Do, re, mi, fa, So, fa, mi, re,
One, two, three, four, Five, four, three, two,

do, Oh, yes it's fun for us to
one. Oh, yes we know that it is

know, So, do, so, ti, so, ti, so, do.
fun, Five, one, five, sev'n, five, sev'n, five, one.

Some of you may like to play the second line of this song on melody flutes, xylophones, violins and piano while the rest of the class is singing this line.

Bring My Flute to Me

Translated by Susanna Myers

French Folk Song

1. Let some-one bring my flute to me And I will play a
2. And don't for-get to bring my drum, I like to beat the

tune, tra la. Let some-one bring my flute to me, And
drum, pom, pom. Then you will march and I will drum; I

you shall hear me play . A mer-ry tune, tra la.
like to beat the drum, . My good old drum, pom, pom.

The Gong and the Drum

Adapted from a Chinese Folk Tune

In my hand a gong, In your hand a drum,

Play them, pret-ty gong and drum. Now we will sing a song,

Bim, bim, bom, bim, bom, Bim, bim, bim, bim, bim, bim, bim, bim, bom.

Listen to "In a Chinese Temple Garden," Ketelbey. (Victor record.)

172

The Shepherd's Tune

L. E. W.

L. E. Watters

so (5) do (8) ti re do la so do mi | re mi fa mi re so

1. A shep-herd boy   would rest at noon, high on the moun-tain side, ·
2. The shep-herd boy   was called to war, high on the moun-tain side. ·

And pipe a-way   a mer-ry tune, high on the moun-tain side. ·
His mel-low flute   is heard no more, high on the moun-tain side. ·

The vil-lage folk for-got their care, high on the moun-tain side, ·
The vil-lage folk are sad at noon, high on the moun-tain side; ·

They knew their flocks were safe up there, high on the moun-tain side. ·
No more they hear this mer-ry tune, high on the moun-tain side. ·

Shepherd's tune. Play it on a melody instrument after each stanza.
merrily

Pasquale[1]

Walter Evans

Brazilian Folk Tune

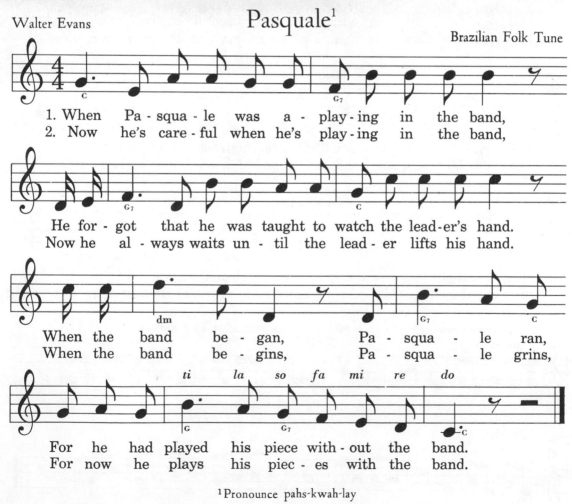

1. When Pa - squa - le was a - play - ing in the band,
2. Now he's care - ful when he's play - ing in the band,

He for - got that he was taught to watch the lead-er's hand.
Now he al - ways waits un - til the lead - er lifts his hand.

When the band be - gan, Pa - squa - le ran,
When the band be - gins, Pa - squa - le grins,

ti la so fa mi re do

For he had played his piece with - out the band.
For now he plays his piec - es with the band.

[1]Pronounce pahs-kwah-lay

Chopsticks

Right hand
Left hand

First player

3/4

(Sing an octave lower than written.)

When I play chop-sticks I play with two fin-gers, With one on my

Right hand

Second player

Left hand

left hand and one on my right.

How many in your room can play this duet on the piano?

175

Susan Blue

Kate Greenaway

Francis Hilliard

First group. (*Voices, violins, flutes and melody instruments.*)

Oh, Su - san Blue, How do you do?

Second group. (*Voices, violins, flutes and melody instruments.*)

Oh, Su - san Blue, How do you

Please may I go for a walk with you?

do? Please may I go for a walk with

Where shall we go? Oh, yes I know,

you? Where shall we go? Oh, yes I

Down in the mead-ow where cow-slips grow.

know, Down in the mead-ow where cow-slips grow.

Susan Blue

First group. (Clarinets or cornets.)

Second group. (Clarinets or cornets.)

Holiday March

For Melody Instruments and Piano

Charles J. Cromwell

Mu - sic, on a hol - i - day, al-ways sounds so grand!

Down the street in col - ors gay comes the band.

Play your flutes and vi - o - lins, horns and trum-pets blow,

While the drum-mers mark the time — here we go!

Marching Song

Christine Turner Curtis

German Folk Tune

1. For - ward, march to the mu - sic. Swing with stead-y stride.
2. For - ward, fol - low the drum-beat Pound-ing loud and strong.

Snare drum, cymbals and other rhythm instruments.

Bass drum.

On - ward, al-ways to-geth - er, March-ing side by side. With the
On - ward, lift up your voic-es, Fill the air with song. While the

shoul-ders square and the head in air While the cym - bals clash and the
ban - ners fly and the heart beats high, And the bells call out to the

snare drums roll. Press on-ward, al-ways to-geth-er. On-ward to the goal.
soar - ing fife. Press on-ward, al-ways to-geth-er. On-ward in-to life.

Latin-American Medley

Gaily

Sticks, woodblocks and drums.

Arranged by Frederick Beckman

Tambourines and maracas.

Slide whistle or siren

1. There was a lit, a   lit, a   lit-tle
2.   1, 2 and 3, 4,   5, 6,   7, 8,
3.   If our · lit-tle sto-ry   is too

boat out in   a   gale,   There was a lit, a   lit, a   lit - tle
9, 10 weeks or   more,   1,   2 and 3, 4,   5, 6,   7, 8,
short for an - y - one,   If   our · lit -tle sto - ry   is   too

boat out in   a   gale,   Oh, there was a lit, a   lit, a   lit - tle
9, 10 weeks or   more,   Oh, 1, 2 and 3, 4,   5, 6,   7, 8,
short for an - y - one,   Oh, if our · lit - tle sto - ry is   too

boat out in a gale; You won't be - lieve it, you won't be -
9, 10 weeks or more; It nev - er came back, it nev - er
short for an - y - one; We'll tell an - oth - er, we'll tell an -

lieve it, You won't be - lieve it could - n't sail.
came back, It nev - er came back to the shore.
oth - er, We'll tell an - oth - er fun - ny one.

Sticks and woodblocks only.

(The carpenters' hammer.)

Cymbal

Cymbal

Sticks, woodblocks and sandblocks.

(Hammers and saws.)

1. The car-pen-ters are work - ing.
2. The help-ers now are com - ing.

Saws now they're tak-ing. They're trim-ming up the lum - ber, Splin-ters they're
Brooms they are bring-ing. They clean up all the shav - ings, Start saws to

mak - ing. They go see, (*Imitate.*) They go saw, (*Imitate.*) And
sing - ing. They go see, (*Imitate.*) They go saw, (*Imitate.*) And

chips and lit - tle piec - es Fall on ev - 'ry draw.
saw - dust fine and gold - en Falls on ev - 'ry draw.

Cymbal   *Cymbal*

Tambourines.

Maracas.   Solo (Six different children, each singing a stanza.)

Come, come and see my farm for it is

love - ly. Come, come and see my farm for it is love - ly.

1. El pol-li-to goes like this, "Peep peep."

El pol-li-to goes like this, "Peep peep." *All* Oh

Sticks, woodblocks, and drum.

Tambourines and maracas.

pas, ca-ma-rade, oh pas, ca-ma-rade, oh pas, oh pas, oh pas; Oh

(Repeat five times.)

pas, ca-ma-rade, oh pas, ca-ma-rade, oh pas, oh pas, oh pas.

(The final ending of this song is on the next page.)

2. El per-ri-to goes like this, "Bow wow." *(repeat)*
3. El gat-i-to goes like this, "Mee- ow." "
4. El bur-ri-to goes like this, "Hee haw." "
5. El pat-i-to goes like this, "Quack, quack." "
6. El chi-chi-to goes like this, "Oink, oink." "

183

El pol - li - to, el per - ri - to, el gat - i - to, el bur - ri - to,

El pat - i - to, el chi - chi - to, they all say, "O - lé!"

The Bird Call

Cheerfully

Frederick Beckman

Melody instruments. (or whistle)

1. I heard a bird call - ing, h'm (or whistle) I
2. I saw him at noon - time, h'm · · I
3. And in the cool eve - ning, h'm · · And

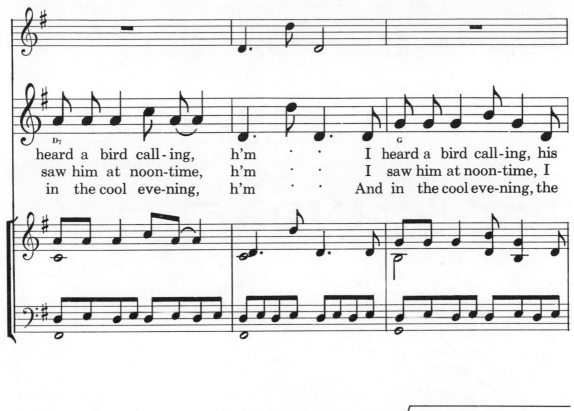

heard a bird call-ing, h'm · · I heard a bird call-ing, his
saw him at noon-time, h'm · · I saw him at noon-time, I
in the cool eve-ning, h'm · · And in the cool eve-ning, the

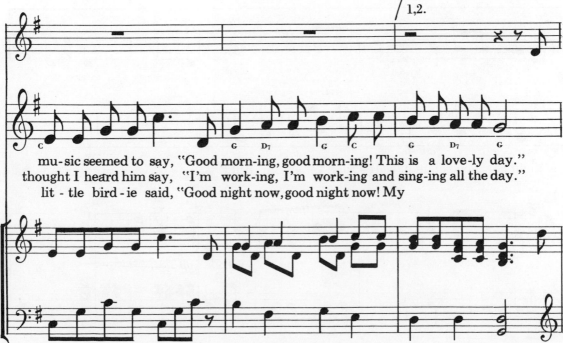

1,2.

mu-sic seemed to say, "Good morn-ing, good morn-ing! This is a love-ly day."
thought I heard him say, "I'm work-ing, I'm work-ing and sing-ing all the day."
lit - tle bird - ie said, "Good night now, good night now! My

chil-dren I have fed; Good

night now, good night now! It's time to go to bed."

Hungarian Dance

After the original by
Blanche Jennings Thompson

Hungarian Folk Song

1. Hi hi ya! hi hi ya! hi hi ya hi!
2. Hi hi ya! hi hi ya! hi hi ya hi!
3. Hi hi ya! hi hi ya! hi hi ya hi!

Choose part-ners, choose part-ners, time hur-ries by!
Change part-ners, change part-ners, now off we fly!
Dance fast-er, dance fast-er, rest by and by!

Swing your part-ner round a-bout, hi hi hi!
Swing your part-ner from the floor, hi hi hi!
Swing your part-ner round a-bout, hi hi hi!

Swing your part-ner round a-bout, hi hi hi!
Swing your part-ner from the floor, hi hi hi!
Swing your part-ner round a-bout, hi hi hi!

Drummer's Medley

Arranged by Frederick Beckman

Flutes and bells play melody.

"Sol - dier boy, sol - dier boy, where are you go - ing,

189

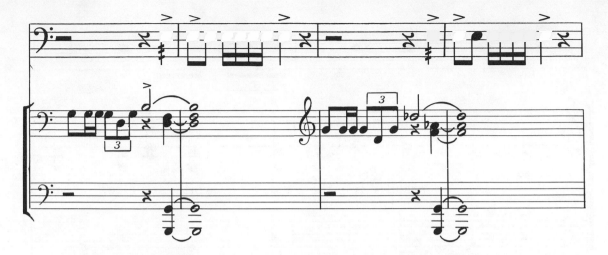

sfz   *pp*

Whistle or play flutes.

Can you

hear the pipes a - play-ing as · the sol-diers march a - long? Can you

hear the drums a-drum-ming to the   rhy-thm of   the song?   It's

far   a-way they go,   the   mu-sic's soft and   low.   Can you

hear the pipes a-play-ing in the   year of Ju - bi-lo? It's   year of Ju- bi-lo?

D.C. al Fine

Hear Them Bells!

G Major Chord   Dominant Seventh Chord

Traditional
Arranged by Frederick Beckman

Lively

Resonator bells.

Hear them bells! · Hear them bells! · Hear them bells! ·

Descant second time only.

Hear them bells, · can't you hear them bells. · They are

Ding dong ding dong, ding dong ding dong,

ring-ing out the glo-ry of the land. (Hal - le - lu - jah, lu - jah.)

Ding dong ding dong, ding dong ding dong,

Hear them bells, · can't you hear them bells, · They are

Ding dong ding dong, ding dong ding dong,

ring-ing out the glo-ry of the land.

Ding dong ding dong, ding, ding, dong.

The Marines' Hymn[1]

Song flutes and voices.

1. From the Halls of Mon-te-zu - ma To the shores of
flag's un-furl'd to ev-'ry breeze From · dawn to
health to you and to our Corps Which · we are

Trip-o - li; · We · fight our coun-try's bat - tles In the
set-ting sun; · We have fought in ev-'ry clime and place Where
proud to serve; · In · many a strife we've fought for life And

air, on land and sea; · First to fight for right and free - dom And to
we could take a gun; · In the snow of far off North-ern lands And in
nev-er lost our nerve; If the Ar-my and the Na - vy Ev-er

keep our hon - or clean; · We are proud to claim the
sun - ny trop-ic scenes, · You will find us al - ways
look on Heav-en's scenes, · They will find the streets are

1,2.
3.

ti - tle Of U - nit-ed States Ma-rines. · 2. Our
on the job, The U - nit-ed States Ma-rines. · 3. Here's
guard-ed By U - nit-ed States Ma- rines.

The Angel Band

South Carolina Folk Song

There was one, there were two, there were three lit - tle an - gels,

There were four, there were five, there were six lit - tle an - gels,

There were sev'n there were eight, there were nine lit - tle an - gels,

Ten lit - tle . an - gels in the band.

CHORUS

Oh, was - n't that a band, Sun - day morn - ing,

Sun - day morn - ing, Sun - day morn - ing.

Was-n't that a band, Sun-day morn-ing,

Sun-day morn-ing so soon.

One Man Went to Mow

Camp Song

One man went to mow, went to mow a mead-ow.

One man and his dog went to mow a mead-ow.

Two men went to mow, went to mow a mead-ow.

*ad lib.

Two men, one man and his dog went to mow a mead-ow.

*Up to any number desired.

197

Quiet Night

Susanna Myers

Spanish Folk Tune

1. Now the shades of eve - ning soft - ly veil the light.
2. Through the hours of dark - ness, while the world's a - sleep

Like a gen - tle moth - er comes the qui - et night:
As a moth - er guard - ing, night her watch will keep.

Calls her wea - ry chil - dren from work and from play;
She will still to si - lence the sounds of the day,

Bids them rest and sleep and dream at close of day.
Hush - ing e - ven thrush - es' song and rob - ins' lay.

SHINING HOURS

Jack and the Beanstalk

By Frank Luther

(Whistle)

Hear that boy whistling? It's Jack. Jack and his mother were poor because a wicked giant came and stole their bag of gold, and their magic harp, and their little hen that laid the golden eggs. All they had left was an old brown cow.

One morning his mother sent Jack to market to trade the old brown cow for some food. Here came Jack home from market.

(Whistle)

His mother said, "Jack, what did you get in trade for the old brown cow?" Jack said,

"I trad-ed my cow for a lit-tle red calf, And

in that trade I lost just half; I trad-ed my calf for a

lit-tle pink pig, It was-n't worth much 'cause it was-n't ver-y big; I

trad-ed my pig for a lit-tle white mouse, He

would-n't say "please" and he would-n't keep house; I trad-ed my mouse for a

lit-tle white bean, The pret-ti-est bean you've ev-er seen."

Jack's mother was so angry, she threw the little white bean out into the yard. Next morning, when Jack looked out the window, he saw a great beanstalk growing in the yard, stretching up and up into the sky as far as he could see. Jack began to climb the beanstalk.

He climbed and he climbed and he climbed and he climbed,

And he climbed and he climbed and he

climbed and he climbed. He climbed and he climbed and he

climbed and he climbed, And he climbed and he climbed

and he climbed and he climbed and he climbed.

Right to the top of the beanstalk. Then he stepped into the Giant's land. Jack went up to the Giant's castle and knocked on the door. Mrs. Giant opened the door. Jack said, "Good morning, Mrs. Giant, my name is Jack." Mrs. Giant said, "Jack, you are a brave boy to come here. Hide in this kettle quickly. Here comes Mr. Giant!" Jack hid in the kettle, and here came the Giant.

Fee, fie, foe, fum, 1, 2, 3 and here I come.

Fum, foe, fie, fee, Here I come with a 1, 2, 3.

"Bring me my little hen that lays the golden eggs." Mrs. Giant brought the little hen and she began to sing.

Cack, cack - a - dack, cack - a - dack, cack - a - dack - et.

As the hen sang, the Giant went to sleep. Jack hopped out of the kettle ... Hopped up on the table ... He grabbed the little hen ... And away he ran. The little hen started to sing.

Cack, cack - a - dack, cack - a - dack, cack - a - dack - et.

This woke up the Giant and he started to chase Jack.

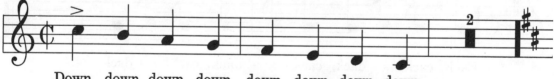

Here came the Gi-ant, clump, clump. Here came the Gi-ant, clump, clump.

Jack climbed down the beanstalk as fast as he could go.

Down, down, down, down, down, down, down, down.

When Jack got to the bottom, he ran in the house and said, "Look, Mother, I've brought back the little hen that the Giant stole from us." The little hen was so glad to be home that she started to sing.

Cack, cack - a - dack, cack - a - dack, cack - a - dack - et.

Jack told his mother goodby, and he began to climb the beanstalk.

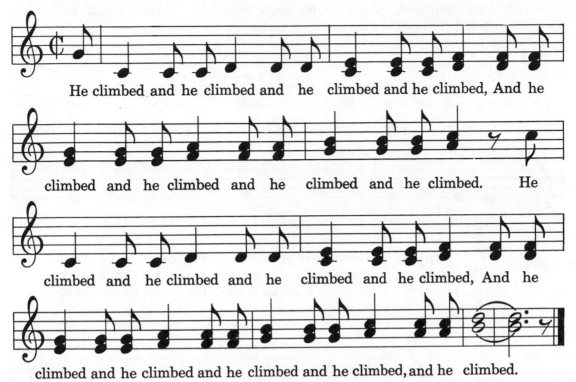

He climbed and he climbed and he climbed and he climbed, And he climbed and he climbed and he climbed and he climbed. He climbed and he climbed and he climbed and he climbed, And he climbed and he climbed and he climbed and he climbed, and he climbed.

When Mrs. Giant saw Jack she said, "The Giant is very angry! Hide in this kettle quickly!" Jack hid in the kettle and here came the Giant.

Fee, fie, foe, fum, 1, 2, 3 and here I come.

The Giant said, "Bring me my magic harp." Mrs. Giant brought the harp and it began to sing.

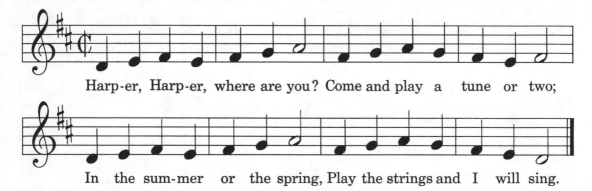

Harp-er, Harp-er, where are you? Come and play a tune or two;

In the sum-mer or the spring, Play the strings and I will sing.

As the harp sang, the Giant went to sleep. Jack hopped out of the kettle ... He hopped up on the table ... He grabbed the harp ... and away he ran. The harp was so happy it began to sing. This woke up the Giant and he began to chase Jack.

Here came the Gi - ant, clump, clump.

Here came the Gi - ant, clump, clump.

Jack climbed down the beanstalk as fast as he could go.

Down, down, down, down, down, down, down, down.

Jack ran in the house and said, "Look, Mother! I've brought back the golden harp the Giant stole from us!" And the harp and the hen were so glad to be home, they sang together.

Cack, cack-a-dack, cack-a-dack, cack-a-dack-et,

Harp

(*Can be played on the piano.*)

Cack, cack-a-dack, cack-a-dack, cack-a-dack-et.

And then Jack started to climb up the beanstalk again.

He climbed and he climbed and he climbed and he climbed, And he

climbed and he climbed and he climbed and he climbed. He

climbed and he climbed and he climbed and he climbed, And he

climbed and he climbed and he climbed and he climbed and he climbed.

Right up to the Giant's Land. Mrs. Giant said, "Jack, hide in this kettle quickly, the Giant is very angry." . . . And here came the Giant.

Fee, fie, foe, fum, 1, 2, 3 and here I come.

"Bring me my moneybag! Money, money, money, sing to me!" And the money sang.

Dia-monds, ru-bies, em-'ralds too, Spar-kling like the sil-ver dew.

Count them o-ver, one by one, Spar-kling like the sun.

As soon as the Giant was asleep, Jack jumped out of the kettle . . . He jumped upon the table . . . He grabbed the moneybag and away he ran. And the moneybag started to sing . . . This woke up the Giant who began to chase Jack.

Here came the Gi-ant, clump, clump. Here came the Gi-ant, clump, clump.

Jack climbed down the beanstalk as fast as he could go.

Down, down, down, down, down, down, down, down.

But this time the Giant climbed down the beanstalk after Jack.

Here came the Gi - ant, clump, clump.

Down, down, down, down, down, down, down, down.

Here came the Gi - ant, clump, clump.

Down, down, down, down, down, down, down, down.

When Jack got to the bottom of the beanstalk, he grabbed the axe and began to chop down the beanstalk.

Chop, chop, chop, chop, hur - ry up, Jack.

Chop, chop, chop, we're glad you're back.

Then the beanstalk fell with a great cra-a-a-sh! ... The Giant bounced back up into the Giant's Land ... And they never saw him again ... And they lived happily ever after.

Sleeping Beauty

By Frank Luther

This is the story of Sleeping Beauty. Once upon a time a little princess was born in Whitestone Castle in a country far, far away. The King said, "Ring out the bells!" People came from far and near to see the little princess.

Some came on horse-back, tee-gal-lop, tee-gal-lop, tee-gal-lop, tee-gal-lop.

Horses' hoof beats.

Some came walk-ing.

Marching feet.

Chil-dren came danc-ing, hop-ping and skip-ping and run-ning and jump-ing, And what were they com-ing to see? The ba-by, the ba-by, the ba-by, the ba-by.

What were they com-ing to see? · The ba - by, that's

what they were com-ing to see. · Soon Whitestone Castle was full of people, and they all brought gifts.

(SOLO I)

The first good fair - y said, "I give her beau - ty."

(SOLO II)

The next good fair - y said, "I give her joy."

(SOLO III)

The next good fair - y said, "I give her kind - ness."

(SOLO IV)

The next good fair - y said, "I give her love."

The bad fair-y said, "I give her six-teen years to

dim. e rit.

live. *Then* she'll stick a nee-dle in her fin-ger, then she'll go to

p   *pp*

sleep   For a hun-dred years."

Well, everyone forgot what the bad fairy said. They named the princess "Beauty." When she grew up and she was sixteen they gave her a birthday party.

1. Hap - py Birth - day, Hap - py Birth - day! Laugh on your
2. [Instrumental only.]
3. Hap - py Birth - day, Hap - py Birth - day! You'll al - ways

1, 2   *3*

birth - day and drive all your cares a - way.

be young as long as this   song is sung.

The King and Queen were danc-ing slow-ly; Bow, turn,

Repeat is instrumental only.

now turn back. The chil - dren were danc-ing;

Hi rig-a-jig and a - way we go. The chil - dren were

danc - ing; Round and a-round and - a to and fro.

Hap - py Birth-day, Hap - py Birth-day! Save your sor-row,

Repeat is instrumental only.

save your tear, you'll get young-er ev -'ry year.

Everyone was happy and dancing. When the Princess saw a needle on the floor she picked it up and the needle stuck her finger!

She said, "I'm sleep-y, I'm go-ing to sleep, and so good night, my dears." · Soon ev-'ry one had gone to sleep, and they slept for a hun-dred years. ·

A hundred years went by. Then, one day, a prince and his merry men came riding through the wood.

Horses' hoof beats in the background.

Tee - gal - lop, tee - gal - lop, tee - gal - lop, tee - gal - lop.

Here came the hunting hounds, running after the fox.

Hounds.

Ouf! Ouf! Ouf! Ouf! Ouf! Ouf! Ouf! Ouf!

Horses' hoof beats and hounds' baying continue softly.

1. Ha - loo, ha - lay; o - ver the hill and far a - way. Ha -
2. Instrumental only.
3. Ha - loo, ha - lye; o - ver the hill and through the rye. Ha -

loo, ha - lee; o - ver the hill with me. Tee -
loo, ha - lo; o - ver the hill we go. Tee -

gal - lop, tee - gal - lop, tee - gal - lop, tee - gal - lop.
gal - lop, tee - gal - lop, tee - gal - lop, tee - gal - lop.

216

When they came to the castle gate, the Prince said, "Stop!" The Prince went into Whitestone Castle and saw everything was asleep.

He saw the birds a-sleep in the trees, the dogs a-sleep by the sta-ble. The cats and mice a-sleep by the door, the roost-er a-sleep on the roof, · The hors-es sleep-ing in the stalls, the trum-pet-ers a-sleep on the floor; · And on the throne he saw the King and Queen fast a-sleep; And then he saw his Sleep-ing Beau-ty sound a-sleep at their feet. ·

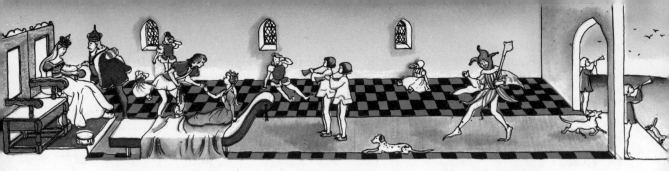

Then the Prince saw the needle in Sleeping Beauty's finger. He pulled the needle out, and Sleeping Beauty woke up! Then everyone woke up!

Bird calls.

The birds woke up in the trees,

Dogs bark.

The dogs woke up by the sta - ble,

Cats meow.

The cats woke up by the door,

Rooster crows.

The roost - er woke up on the roof,

Horses neigh.

The hors - es woke up in the barn,

The trum-pet-ers blew their trum-pets.

218

This woke up the King and Queen. The King said, "Young Prince, if my daughter loves you she shall be your bride." The princess said she did, so the wedding bells rang out. And the wedding dance began.

Marching feet.

The King danced with the Queen,

The trum-pet-ers danced with the cooks,

Rooster crows.

The roost-er danced on the roof,

Horses neigh.

The hors-es danced in the barn,

The dogs ran aft-er the cats, The cats ran aft-er the

rats and mice, The boys and girls and an - i - mals all

danced a - round the hall.

(One of you can play this on the piano while others dance.)

And the Prince and Sleeping Beauty lived happily ever after.

Now you've heard the sto - ry, How Sleep - ing Beau - ty

went to sleep, to sleep, to sleep.

ALPHABETICAL INDEX

Recorded songs are identified by the album numbers (4–A), (4–B), and (4–C).
Titles in italics indicate instrumental selections.